At the Mercy of Nature

Shackleton's Survival Saga
Gives Promise for Our Future

Carl N. McDaniel

Illustrations by Donald Watson

Sigel Press

for
Ellie, Gus, Ben, and Ruth
who will know we did our best

Sigel Press
4403 Belmont Court
Medina, Ohio 44256

51A Victoria Road
Cambridge CB4 3BW
England

Visit us on the World Wide Web at www.sigelpress.com

Cover design: Donald Watson, Kate Alter and Harp Mando
Internal design: Harp Mando
Typesetting: Professional Book Compositors, Inc., Lorain Ohio

ISBN: 978-1-905941-20-9

Printed in the United States of America

Printed on 100% recycled, 100% post-consumer waste paper.

Contents

List of Illustrations

Sources and credits for illustrations: The illustrations of Shackleton's journey are based upon photographs of Frank Hurley, which have become the iconic representations of the *Endurance* Party, along with paintings by *Endurance* artist George Marston. Sun and weather conditions are depicted as they could have occurred. Journal entries describe the clarity of light and serenity of seas at exhilarating moments, adding dramatic contrast to the party's precarious state. You can find the sources for illustrations in the Notes for the page on which the illustration appears.

Acknowledgements

I have had this project in mind and on my desk for a long time. My first debt is to Alfred Lansing for writing a most engaging book, Endurance: *Shackleton's Incredible Voyage.* I read his book in the 1990s and was struck by their unlikely survival—none should have lived. In time, I realized that global civilization had sailed into its own Weddell Sea pack ice giving rise to challenges that mirrored well those encountered by the *Endurance* Party. I believe Shackleton and his *Endurance* Party made the impossible, possible. This is exactly what modern societies need to do in many arenas, especially environmental challenges—climate change, biodiversity and life-support loss, over population and consumption, and our dysfunctional political-economic system in terms of how it relates to these four mega environmental issues.

My special thanks go to Donald Watson for his years of unwavering support, for his insightful critique of draft manuscripts, for his generous offer to make the book come alive with his engaging illustrations, and for his insistence on me to state the book's essence in half a dozen words. Hence the title: *At the Mercy of Nature.*

Rensselaer Polytechnic Institute granted me a sabbatical for academic year 2006-07 during which the writing of this book began and without which I suspect the book would not have been written. I am indebted to Oberlin College's Environmental Studies Department for giving me an academic home and support for completing *At the Mercy of Nature.*

I thank three Oberlin students—Josh Laufer, Rachel McMonagle, David Riddel—who took a private reading course with me at Oberlin College that provided many discussions on and analyses of why the *Endurance* Party survived. I am grateful for the varied insights and criticisms given draft manuscripts by David Borton, Harriet Borton, Ann Craig, Norm Craig, Anne Elder, John Elder, George Ficke, Robert Longsworth, Reg Morrison, David Orr, David Sonner, and David Young. Howard Stoner, a student of Antarctic exploration, provided commentary and suggestions on drafts thereby providing important information and perspectives. David Benzing gave two drafts his detailed, no-holds-barred, professorial treatment that improved the presentation immensely for which I am most appreciative.

I cannot say enough about Kelly Viancourt who enthusiastically supported the project and who thoroughly edited the best draft I could produce. With skill she cut the unnecessary and used her superb editing ability to make what remained into a coherent, readable text. Thomas Sigel then used his considerable talent and experience to polish the text and oversee the assembly of the book before you.

Mary, my wife, witnessed and participated in the gestation and birthing of four books from her husband, who never intended to write even one. Our friends call her a saint and she is.

The people mentioned above, and others, did their best to have me write only that which is true, but errors and misstatements remain for which I am responsible.

Prelude

The Weddell Sea Party of the failed Imperial Trans-Antarctic Expedition led by Sir Ernest Shackleton (1914–1916) is the most notable survival story in recorded history. Scaled down from 7 billion people to 28 men, it depicts well humanity's dire straits and a way through. Everything is there: unrelenting forces of nature at their worst; situations never before encountered; an absolutely unknowable future; severely constrained and limited resources; a diverse mix of human personalities; unimaginable physical and emotional challenges and hardships; decisions both excellent and poor; good and bad luck; and most importantly, the effective leadership, cooperation, and discipline combined with an unflinching acceptance of evidence-based reality required to survive.

In Part 1, I retell the story of the Weddell Sea Party in some detail to give the reader an appreciation of what Shackleton and his men achieved and why everyone considers the survival of all 28 men an extraordinary accomplishment. In Part 2, I consider why they survived when that outcome was highly unlikely. In Part 3, I argue that humanity is challenged by a handful of interdependent situations similar to those faced by the *Endurance* Party, and that the reasons for their success provide guidelines we would be wise to follow.

PART 1
STORY OF THE *ENDURANCE* PARTY

On December 5, 1914, Sir Ernest Shackleton, along with 27 men aboard the ship *Endurance*, departed South Georgia Island in the southern Atlantic Ocean for Vahsel Bay on the northeast coast of Antarctica. Twenty-one months later, on August 30, 1916, the *Yelcho*, a Chilean government ship with Shackleton on board, picked up 22 men on the northeast coast of Elephant Island. What follows is a retelling of what happened between those two dates.

CHAPTER 1

Adrift in the Weddell Sea

The men had retired to their tents when Boss announced, "She's going, boys!" All scrambled out to look. The mastless, broken *Endurance* had finally been freed from the sea's icy grip. The ship's bow descended as her stern rose 20 feet into the air, silhouetted against the late afternoon sky. A moment later the ship slipped silently into the deep. From atop his lookout tower at Ocean Camp, Boss quietly pronounced, "She's gone, boys."

The men—28 in all—were perched on an ice floe measuring just 1 square mile, stranded hundreds of miles from the coast of Antarctica in the Weddell Sea. Then, and for most of the remainder of their journey, not a single other person had ever been where they were. No one in the world knew of their shipwreck, and the stranded explorers had no methods of communication. They were utterly alone—a tiny speck of humanity in 1 million square miles of floating ice and snow. It was November 21, 1915. The Weddell Sea Party of the Imperial Trans-Antarctic Expedition, organized by Sir Ernest Henry Shackleton, now had an entirely new agenda—to survive.

The expedition had been promoted as an important scientific endeavor. Shackleton's calling, however, was Antarctica and the opportunity to undertake what no one else had done thereby gaining wealth and fame. Could Great Britain regain the glory of polar exploration? Robert Peary, an American, had reached the North Pole in 1909 and Roald Amundsen, a Norwegian, the South Pole in 1911. "There now remains the largest and most striking of all journeys—the crossing of the continent," Shackleton wrote.

His plan was simple, yet bold and imaginative. The *Endurance* would sail into the Weddell Sea and drop a team of six men at Vahsel Bay on the eastern edge of Antarctica. The men would sledge to the pole and then continue across Antarctica to McMurdo Sound, following an expedition route

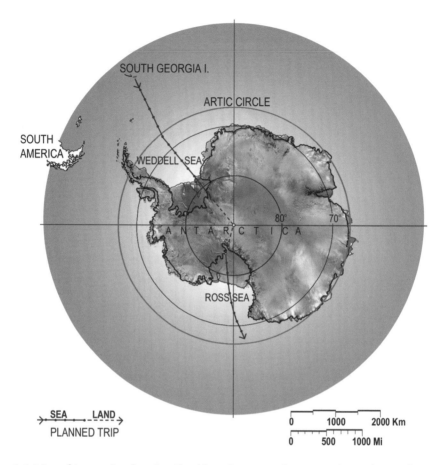

1.1: Map of Antarctica showing Shackleton's proposed transcontinental route from Vahsel Bay at the base of the Weddell Sea to the South Pole and the return to the camp at McMurdo Sound in the Ross Sea.

which Shackleton and Robert Scott had taken years earlier. Shackleton knew from experience that the Weddell Sea Party couldn't transport sufficient supplies for its entire 1,800-mile journey—Scott's team had starved to death in 1912 on its return from the pole, and Shackleton's earlier party in 1909 had turned back before ever reaching its destination. To avoid these failures this time, Shackleton arranged for a second team, this one aboard the *Aurora,* to enter the Ross Sea and establish a base at McMurdo Sound. From there they would lay supply depots for the Weddell Sea Party during their return from the pole.

Shackleton became famous following his Antarctic expedition in 1908-09, when he trekked to within 97 miles of the South Pole. Perhaps his team could have reached the pole, but they surely would have died of cold and starvation on their return. Valuing his men's welfare more than his goal, Shackleton had turned back. Even so, starvation was a constant threat. The men struggled against cold, blizzards, exhaustion, and illness to reach the depots of food they had cached on their outbound journey. At one point when he and Frank Wild were suffering from starvation and dysentery, Wild wrote in his diary:

> [Shackleton] privately forced upon me his one breakfast biscuit, and would have given me another tonight had I allowed him. I do not suppose that anyone else in the world can thoroughly realize how much generosity and sympathy were shown by this: I do, and by God I shall never forget it. Thousands of pounds would not have bought that one biscuit.

Time and again, Boss put his men's needs before his own. This character trait was a hallmark of his leadership.

Shackleton returned to England a hero in 1909, knighted by the king of England and acknowledged with honors by many nations. He wrote a book and toured North America and Europe as the quintessential polar explorer. However, he grew bored with the customs of the civilized world and was not altogether successful at dealing with them. He yearned for the ice-bound world that pitted one against the implacable forces of nature.

Groundwork for his 1914 expedition took the second half of 1913. In January 1914, with the promise of financial backing, Shackleton announced his plans. Some 5,000 applicants, including three women, sought out one of the 56 positions on the *Endurance* team and the Ross Sea Party, but Shackleton required few new recruits. He built much of his crew from the pool of hardened veterans of exploration and adventure that he already knew. Of the interviews he actually conducted, few if any, lasted more than 5 minutes. He had an uncanny ability to size up a man quickly. The major criterion appeared to be whether or not Shackleton liked a man, a liking that related to the man's character and hardiness. However, the system wasn't perfect. Shackleton dismissed the *Endurance* cook and three seamen from duty and replaced them at Buenos Aires.

Of the new hires, none was more fortuitous than Frank Worsley, a ship captain who would soon become the *Endurance's* skipper. Worsley, based in London at the time, dreamed one night that he was navigating his ship down Burlington Street—amid huge pieces of ice. A superstitious man, he took the dream as a premonition and proceeded to Burlington Street the next day. An office sign caught his attention: "Imperial Trans-Antarctic Expedition." Inside, he found Shackleton. Worsley wrote:

> He and I spent only a few minutes together, but the moment that I set eyes on him I knew that he was a man with whom I should be proud to work. He quickly divined what I wanted, and presently said to me, "You're engaged. Join your ship until I wire for you. I'll let you know all details as soon as possible. Good morning." He wrung my hand in his hard grasp, and that was that.

The *Endurance* had its captain.

Worsley sailed the *Endurance* to Buenos Aires. Shackleton and Wild, the expedition's second in command, met the ship there. After a few weeks of stocking and preparations, the ship departed for South Georgia Island on October 26, 1914.

After several days at sea, Perce Blackborow, a stowaway, revealed himself to become the 28th man in the Weddell Sea Party. Third Officer Alfred Cheetham, age 47, was the oldest. The three youngest were 22: Blackborow, assistant to the cook; Ernest Holness, fireman; and A.J. Kerr, second engineer. The three leaders of the team—Shackleton, Wild, and Worsley—were 40, 41, and 42. The average shipmate age was 31.

The *Endurance* reached the whaling stations at Grytviken, South Georgia, on November 5, 1914. The Antarctic whalers there were keen on the expedition and more than willing to share all they knew of the southern waters and its ice. The Weddell Sea is a several million-square-mile area of ocean roughly between 65° and 75° south latitude, and 20° and 60° west longitude. As the indentation that the Atlantic Ocean makes into Antarctica, the Weddell Sea is 1,300 miles wide at its northern mouth and extends 600 miles to the south. Vahsel Bay, Shackleton's planned jumping-off place, is 1,600 miles almost due south from South Georgia at the southernmost end of the Weddell Sea. Interior to what is now the Caird Coast is Coats Land that stretches 600 miles to the northeast of Vahsel Bay. Eleven hundred miles to the northwest of Vahsel Bay, across the Weddell Sea, is Graham Land and the Larsen Ice Shelf.

Sea ice is always present in the Weddell Sea, and often impenetrable. The band of ice along the coast varies in width and thickness from season to season and year to year. During the severest winters, pack ice fills the sea and extends north and northeast to the South Sandwich Islands group.

Water currents push the ice west and northwest against the Graham Land coast, causing the entire ice mass to move in a clockwise circle. Once formed, ice remains for several years, and because winds are less intense than in other parts of Antarctica, lingers on into summer.

The whaler captains who had recently returned from Antarctic waters warned Shackleton that the Weddell Sea ice had never been as treacherous. Owing to these exceptionally severe conditions, some of the whaling skippers were skeptical that the *Endurance* could reach Antarctica. They advised Shackleton to lay over until the next summer. This was unthinkable. He agreed to give the ice one month to clear a bit.

During his layover, Shackleton met Thoralf Sørlle, a Norwegian who managed the Stromness whaling factory. Sørlle had spent his earlier days harpooning whales and had vast experience with polar ice. He admired the *Endurance* but had concerns about her design. He worried that the ice might crush her.

Known first as the *Polaris*, shipbuilders in the Framnaes shipyard in Norway constructed the *Endurance* for an entrepreneur to take wealthy clients on Arctic polar bear hunting parties. Finances fell short, however, leading the *Polaris*'s owner, who liked Shackleton and took an interest in

1.2: *Endurance* at anchor.

his daring expedition, to sell him the ship at a discounted price of $67,000. Shackleton renamed her for his family's motto: *Fortitudine vincimus*, "By endurance we conquer."

The Framnaes shipyard had built many ships for polar exploration, including the *Fram* used by the Amundsen party, but adventures into polar waters had waned. In fact, the builders had anticipated that *Endurance* would be their last ship of this type, so they gave her special attention. A handsome barkentine of three masts: foremast square rigged and aft masts schooner-like, with sails fore and aft, she measured 144 feet, with a 25-foot beam. A 350-horsepower, coal-fired steam engine gave her a maximum speed of 10.2 knots.

The *Endurance* was perhaps the strongest wooden ship ever built in Norway—maybe even anywhere—with the possible exception of the *Fram*. The *Fram* was constructed with a round bottom to assure that it could be pushed up and out of the ice, rather than be crushed by it. Sørlle noted that the sides of the *Endurance* were more walled than the *Fram's*, a bit like those of a standard ship. He worried that the more vertical sides above the rounded bottom might give ice under extreme pressure sufficient grip to hold and crush the ship. While the *Endurance* was well-suited to operate in the loose ice of the Arctic, he thought it might not withstand the solid ice of Antarctica.

Nevertheless, a determined Shackleton set sail from South Georgia on December 5, 1914, heading for Vahsel Bay in the southeast part of the Weddell Sea. Taking the whalers' advice, he headed through and beyond the Sandwich Group to avoid the impassable pack ice to the south. By entering the Weddell Sea from the northeast, he hoped to slip down the eastern side of the pack into an ice-free Vahsel Bay during the summer thaw.

The *Endurance* could travel 200 miles a day in the open ocean, but in ice, the distance averaged 30 miles or less. Even so, the plan was to reach shore by late December.

Side Note 1.

- The shape of the hull made crushing *Endurance* possible but not the *Fram*.
- In 1896, Svante Arrhenius established that increasing the atmospheric carbon dioxide (CO_2) level would warm the planet significantly.
- Crushing of *Endurance* and warming of the planet are both derived from basic principles of physics.

1.3: The *Endurance* Party's last view of civilization at Stromness whaling station on South Georgia Island before sailing into the ice-filled Weddell Sea.

December was summer in the Antarctic, with 24 hours of sun. At dusk, the moisture in the air froze into tiny crystals of an infinite variety of shapes that glittered in enchantingly beautiful ice showers. The immense expanses of snow and ice that stretched to the horizon, and the sea itself, teemed with life: whales—finner, humpback, blue, killer—and birds—terns, fulmars, prions, pigeons, petrels, albatrosses, and penguins of many species, including emperors and Adélies. Weddell and crabeater seals slept on the snow-covered ice. Countless microscopic diatoms, the base of the food web, gave the local Antarctic waters a deep olive-green color and undercoated the ice floes with a yellow-brown hue.

Perhaps only those who have sailed among the Antarctic floes can appreciate the majestic, surreal beauty and ever-present danger during the *Endurance's* passage south and west toward Vahsel Bay. Pictures by Frank Hurley, the expedition's photographer, and diaries and books written by those who were present, provide glimpses of what they saw. Worsley wrote:

Great blocks of ice, fantastic shapes of blue, green and white, rose and fell with amazing swiftness and violence on all sides of us. It seemed impossible that our deeply laden ship could live through it. …

There was a continual rainbow-like variety of colour. … [W]e experienced colour in a way unknown outside the far North or South. It was as though our snowy surroundings were being painted upon continually by a master-hand, or the most superb lime-lights were being played upon us.

Worsley was fascinated by the spectacular red and gold parhelia, or mock-suns, that appeared as bright spots on a halo around the sun. Each had a straight, colored line running through it, sometimes joining another parhelion on the opposite side of the halo. "When you gazed upon this strange and awe-inspiring sky, you felt as though you had stepped into a world where the laws of Nature, as you had known them, were suspended and overruled by some vaster Power, which was thus making itself known to you." These images were created by refraction through ice crystals in the atmosphere.

1.4: *Endurance* enters Weddell Sea pack ice for which the crew was prepared, confident they'd accomplish their goal.

Progress was slow. Christmas and New Year's Day came and went, with the ship still positioned hundreds of miles from Vahsel Bay. Ice was everywhere. Brittle and young, it easily yielded to the *Endurance's* prow. On January 9, 2015, the sailors passed an iceberg that stood 150 feet above the surface, dwarfing them, yet to the south and west, open, clear waters extended to the horizon. Worsley noted, "We feel as pleased as Balboa when, having burst through the forest of the Isthmus [of Panama], he beheld the Pacific." At full speed they steamed south. Late afternoon the next day, they saw land. Shackleton named it Caird Coast for James Caird, the expedition's most generous financial backer. At midnight, some 500 feet from the 1,000-foot ice cliffs of Antarctica, they headed west.

For 5 days they sailed along the barrier ice cliffs toward Vahsel Bay, some 200 miles distant. On the sixth day—January 16, 1915—they encountered heavy pack ice apparently immobilized by grounded icebergs. An east-northeast gale settled in, forcing the men to seek refuge in the lee of a

1.5: From the bow of the *Endurance* the men see pack ice all around but still remain confident.

stranded berg. On January 18 the pack opened enough to permit another 10 miles of progress, but then gave way to more heavy ice. Entering the pack, the crew sensed these floes were different—deep snow covered the thick ice, and between floes an ice-soup of ground-up pack required full power to penetrate. The ship passed two large floes that evening and entered a pool, but the ice soon closed around them. They waited for an opening, but a strong northeast wind blew for 6 cloudy, rainy days. Afterwards, impenetrable pack ice was evident in every direction. To the south and east, some 16 miles, Antarctica was visible as a world of ice cliffs.

The next day, January 25, a lead in the ice opened 50 yards ahead, but with sails set and the engines at full throttle, the *Endurance* wouldn't budge. A northeast wind had pushed thousands of square miles of ice hard against the northern coast of Antarctica, and the *Endurance* was holding fast in its midst. The ship's crew continued with its normal routine and watches while waiting for a southerly gale to disperse the ice.

Although no one held out much hope, the men set up their listening radio on January 31. A station on the Falkland Islands was to broadcast time checks and news at designated times, but at 1,650 miles away, the crew heard only static. Several times in February, when leads opened near the *Endurance*, the men made valiant efforts to free the ship. They failed, but the challenge of trying to escape brought them closer together. Winter was coming. On February 17 the sun dipped momentarily below the horizon. After a few months, 24-hour days would become 24-hour nights that would last for 3 months. The temperature dropped below zero degrees Fahrenheit.

Still, the men's spirits remained high, and no one besides Shackleton was the least bit concerned when a single watchman replaced sea watches of several men. These explorers welcomed the opportunity to get a full night's sleep. The ice-trapped *Endurance* drifted within 60 miles of Vahsel Bay and

Side Note 2.
- The *Endurance* was beset and the crew knew they would have to spend winter on the ice.
- In the late 1950s climate scientists knew the CO_2 concentration was 10 percent higher than in preindustrial times.
- In both cases, the new knowledge was accepted by those involved without much concern.

1.6: The crew made valiant attempts to free the *Endurance* to no avail.

then, the ice with the ship in its grip, moved away. Shackleton knew then that the Imperial Trans-Antarctic Expedition would have to winter-over on the ice.

Pack ice is a jigsaw puzzle composed of innumerable pieces of ice that the current, wind, and the resulting pressure constantly rearrange and re-shape. Winds, often in excess of 100 miles per hour, push the pack hard against the coast of Antarctica or its grounded icebergs, forcing increasingly more ice into a fixed area. Like tectonic plates, the floes move past, under, and over each other. At times they do battle at their borders—floes rise up tens of feet until they break and then collapse into pressure ridges of ice shards and packed snow. These pressure-driven rearrangements of ice against ice generate all manner of sounds familiar to the human ear. Worsley wrote, "We heard tapping as from a hammer, grunts, groans and squeaks, electric trains running, birds singing, kettles boiling noisily, and an occasional swish as a large piece of ice, released from pressure, suddenly jumped or turned over." During the fall and into winter, pressure events surrounded the *Endurance*, but the floe that immobilized the ship was thick and spared the ship.

1.7: The *Endurance* beset in Weddell Sea ice.

Life slowed as the men adjusted to a hunter-gatherer pace of life in which 3 or 4 hours were sufficient to accomplish all tasks. The remaining hours became free time for reading, game playing, talking, and daydreaming. With the trappings of modern life gone, or absent as in the case of hunter-gatherers, the biggest task was acquiring food. In February, the ice floes of the Weddell Sea teemed with what the explorers needed: meat to eat and blubber for fuel to warm the ship and cook. Seals were the best. Weighing some 400 pounds, a single animal provided plenty of both commodities. Hundreds of seals lounged on the floes around the *Endurance*. In the water, killer whales and sea leopards—large carnivorous seals—both of which were known to take a man down, preyed on seals. On the floes, however, the seals had no enemies—they did not recognize humans as dangerous. The men could calmly approach the animal and stun it with a blow to the head and slit its throat, or just shoot it in the head. Once killed, the men had to quickly dress the seal because its warmth prevented frostbitten hands. Hunting was good. By mid-April the men had accumulated 5,000 pounds of meat and blubber, about a 90-day supply.

The *Endurance* carried 69 Canadian huskies, marginally domesticated wolves, to pull sledges across the continent. When ice beset the ship, the dog teams proved invaluable for hauling killed seals back for butchering. In April, Shackleton assigned permanent dog team drivers to take on responsibility for their teams. Training became major entertainment. A boast from Hurley that his team was the fastest led to a derby. Racing became the rage. Boss encouraged it and participated enthusiastically. He'd learned early in his maritime career that entertainment was invaluable to a crew's wellbeing and morale. The men also put on regular plays and concerts. When interviewing Reginald James for the position of physicist, Shackleton asked if he could sing. James didn't know how to answer. Shackleton then revealed his intent, "Oh, I don't mean any Caruso stuff, but I suppose you can shout a bit with the boys?"

All this time, the *Endurance* was moving in a clockwise direction with the ice. In March, the ice floated west-northwest, but, as April proceeded it eased into a steady northwest drift. On May 2, Worsley determined they had drifted 130 miles, a speed of 2.5 miles per day for the past 2 months. As the days shortened, seals and penguins began migrating north, following the sun. It took Worsley's sharp eyes in the crow's nest to spot the few stragglers. Week two of May saw the sun set without coming back up—the Antarctic night had arrived.

Desolation doesn't convey well the reality of the men's situation, but their activities and diary entries indicate no depression, concern, nor uneasiness. The endless polar night appeared to unite them in common purpose. No one doubted that they'd see the sun return and the expedition continue. The *Endurance* Party—11 crew, two surgeons, and 15 leaders, officers, and scientists—was an eclectic mix, an agglomeration of well-educated university scholars, naval and merchant marine officers, deck hands, skilled engineers, a cook, a carpenter, an artist, and a photographer. Their interests were diverse, and their personalities in some cases were extreme. This community that Shackleton had assembled and groomed thrived during their months of isolated togetherness, contrary to the experiences of other stranded expeditions in which depression, infighting, and even anarchy resulted.

Thomas Orde-Lees was hired on as the motor expert for the powered sledges. Later he became storekeeper. Having been the physical education director of His Majesty's Royal Marines, he could have bested any of the other 27 men. Although a frequent victim of verbal abuse, especially from the seamen, he never rose to the challenge. Interestingly, none of the men wrote of physical fighting or aggression. They did, however, yell and curse at each other, especially later, after leaving the *Endurance's* warm, comfortable shelter.

Orde-Lees had a mysterious, childlike personality and a streak of laziness—he shirked duty without qualm. He was servile, submissive, and compliant to Boss. Like everybody else, Shackleton intensely disliked him when he got to know him on the expedition. Shipmates regarded Orde-Lees a fool. At the same time, Orde-Lees kept a very detailed diary and, under their circumstances of making do with what little food they had, proved to be an exceptional storekeeper. In fact, Shackleton admonished him several times for dispensing too little food.

In contrast, Second Officer Tom Crean stood out as a stalwart of the expedition. A product of the regular navy, the soft-spoken Crean attained stature on an earlier Scott expedition by hiking alone some 30 miles to save a man's life. Tall and almost gaunt, he was a heavy-handed, straight-forward, tactless, disciplined sailor with little warmth who knew his job and the sea. He was uniformly respected. Shackleton liked him for his willingness to do whatever asked and for his discipline. He continuously proved his worth on this expedition.

All in the party considered the cook, Charles Green, a little "off." He had a high, squeaky voice, and although disorganized and scatterbrained, he was overly conscientious. He arguably worked harder than anybody else, save Shackleton. He arrived in the galley before anyone was awake—except the man on watch—and stayed late in the evening. No matter what was happening, Green ensured the men had food and hot drinks. Regardless of conditions or the fun shipmates poked at him—at the time all ships' cooks took a verbal beating—he sported a cheerful grin. On occasion he responded to ribbing in kind. He put frosting on a balloon for a birthday cake and decorated a block of wood for another. The men liked him, as did Shackleton, because he did his job well.

As winter approached, darkness and cold engulfed the *Endurance*. The average temperature in June was minus 17°. Moonlit nights were spectacularly beautiful. The stratospheric ionic lights of the *aurora australis* awed the men with their pulsating colors of blue, green, and silver that cast across the black sky and reflected off ice and snow ever so subtly in different hues. Beneath the floes, marine life was shielded and carried on, albeit at reduced levels. On the ice, however, vanishingly little life persisted. The *Endurance* provided an oasis, a human cocoon in this alien world.

Before the *Endurance* was beset, the officers and scientists had lived in the deckhouse. The sailors' quarters were on the deck below in the forecastle forward of the ship's 35-by-25-foot storeroom. In February, the men moved the stores up to the deckhouse and converted the storeroom to a general gathering place they called the Ritz. Harry McNeish, the carpenter, erected partitions to make sleeping spaces for officers and scientists on the sides.

1.8: Map of Antarctica, Weddell Sea, and the path of the *Endurance* Party.

In the center was a long table that the men used for eating, reading, writing, game playing, and just talking. A paraffin-burning lamp hung over the table, and a coal and blubber-burning stove warmed the space. The 1½- to-3-foot-thick-sides of the *Endurance* provided some insulation against the cutting winds and brutal cold.

Throughout the fall, the ship drifted uneventfully to the northwest. Life had a pleasant routine. The men ate their meals at regular times, and all gathered for tea every afternoon at 4 in the Ritz. The men played hockey, soccer, trained dog teams, and hunted. On Saturday evenings they shared grog in the Ritz, toasting their "sweethearts and wives" with the added chorus, "May they never meet." Sunday evenings meant concerts from the phonograph. Each month Frank Hurley gave a lantern slide talk on places he had photographed: Antarctica, Australia, New Zealand, and the most-often-requested "Peeps in Java"—Pacific Island palms and scantly clad natives. Life was good. The men rolled dice to establish who would buy what when they celebrated their homecoming.

In late June, the ice, from far away at first, began sending strange sounds through the cold, dense, night air—distant, low-pitched roars of ice against ice. On July 9 the barometer read 29.79. For the next 5 days, it dropped steadily, and reached 28.88 on July 14. A huge storm was brewing. The evening prior, Wild and Worsley had chatted with Shackleton in his cabin:

> "She's pretty near her end," Shackleton concluded.
>
> "You mean that the ship will go?" Worsley asked.
>
> "I do," he answered. After a long pause, he added, "The ship can't live in this, Skipper. … Wild and I know how you feel about the *Endurance*, but what the ice gets, the ice keeps."
>
> Wild cheerily added, "Yes, but we are not going to let the ice get us. The poor little *Endurance* may have to go, but we won't."
>
> Lionel Greenstreet, First Officer, knocked and entered, "The play can begin, Sir, whenever you are ready."

In the early hours of July 15, 70-mile-per-hour winds lashed the *Endurance* and blew snow into every nook and cranny—the snow's penetration was unstoppable. A man couldn't see the ship at 50 yards. Boss ordered all hands to venture no farther than the dog kennels. The temperature was minus 34°. Snow piled up in 14-foot drifts on the windward side, pushing the portside down with the added tons of weight. The *Endurance* settled a foot. Fearing the sinking of the floe on the portside and taking the dog kennels with it, Shackleton ordered all men to turn-to and clear the snow.

Side Note 3.
- With the arrival of the first pressure event, the leaders knew the ship was likely to be crushed—they began planning for the new situation.
- In 1968, 10 years of data from the Keeling Curve (the plot of atmospheric CO_2 concentration atop Mauna Loa on Hawaii) established that the concentration of this important heat-trapping gas had increased 2.5 percent—humanity was rapidly increasing the atmospheric concentration of this gas.
- Both of these conclusions are based on fundamental principles of physics.

The storm subsided the next morning, and bits of blue sky appeared on the horizon. The pack had been solid horizon to horizon, but the storm out of Antarctica had created chaos. The floes had broken apart and crashed together to create spectacular ice formations and pressure ridges everywhere. The men saw areas of open water to the north. The innumerable mounds of ice and broken-apart floes made conditions perfect for the wind to catch and push floe against floe across endless miles—thereby creating immense pressure.

The crew could see the ice's turmoil everywhere. Greenstreet and Wild stopped to watch a 9-foot-thick floe drive against a similarly thick ice mass. Effortlessly, the floes rose together into the air as if weightless—up, up, up they danced, belly to belly. Could the *Endurance* withstand the forces behind such motions?

The heavy thick floe entrapping the *Endurance* had protected her, but distant sounds of ice on ice now gave warning. On July 22, the *Endurance's* floe came under intense pressure and cracked from its edge to within 35 yards of the ship. Shackleton noted:

This crack was the result of heavy pressure 300 yards away on the port bow, where huge blocks of ice were piled up in wild and threatening confusion. The pressure at that point was enormous. … Our long months of rest and safety seemed to be at an end, and a period of stress had begun.

Two things were happening. The pack was loosening as if it might break up to free them. Additionally, fierce winds were creating monumental pressure that could crush the *Endurance*. Boss set sea watches to be prepared for whatever might happen. The sun returned for a few moments on July 26 to raise spirits, but the pressure persisted—giant pieces of ice weighing tons were thrown up effortlessly like billowing clouds. Six days later the floe holding the *Endurance* broke up, and momentarily the ship floated. Immediately, though, other floes closed in to jostle her like a toy—for 15 tense minutes she was knocked about. Then, mercifully, she was shoved onto a piece of the old floe that had held her fast for months. The pressure eased off and, by the next afternoon, ceased almost completely. An unscathed *Endurance* continued drifting north.

Several days later Shackleton overheard several men boasting that their ship was up to whatever pressure it might encounter. Boss sat down with them and said:

1.9: The return of the sun to the beset *Endurance* lifted the crew's spirits.

There once was a mouse who lived in a tavern. One night the mouse found a leaky barrel of beer, and he drank all he could hold. When the mouse finished, he sat up, twirled his whiskers, and looked around arrogantly. "Now then," he said, "where's that damned cat?"

Only Wild and Worsley knew that Boss believed the ship would not survive the ice. Without betraying that assessment, Shackleton wanted to dispel the others of misplaced confidence.

The men had seen the pressure of the ice effortlessly flip 50-ton floes and play with the *Endurance* as if she were made of balsa wood. Yet reality still eluded them. They remained upbeat and confident that their ship was immune. Strong southerly winds persisted, and by mid-August the ship had drifted another 160 miles north.

Two uneventful weeks ended abruptly at midnight on August 30—a pressure shock hit, leaving a thin crack in the floe astern. Another jolt hit at dawn. The crack widened to half an inch. Ice was on the move. By evening the immense pressure transmitted through the ice to the *Endurance's* hull was causing her to creak and wail mournfully. The crew could see the floes shifting ahead. All night ice inched along the port side with haunting, unsettling sounds—moaning, screeching, grinding. Most of the men didn't sleep. In the afternoon the pressure intensified, and by evening the ship shivered and quaked. Timbers groaned. Deck planking and beams buckled, crackling and scraping as they were contorted. In the wee hours the ship jumped and shook, startling the few men still able to sleep. As dawn broke the unnerving sounds of the past 3 days slipped away. The pressure eased. Miraculously the ice had not penetrated—the *Endurance* was tested again and found resilient.

It was September, the end of winter. Temperatures eased above freezing. Robert Clark, the expedition's biologist, noted an increase in plankton in the middle of the month. A few days later, when some men were exercising several dog teams on a trip to a berg 7 miles from the ship, they sighted a seal for the first time in 5 months. They quickly killed it to augment dwindling stores. More than 10 hours of sun lifted spirits, yet as October approached, the men became anxious. Twice before, the ice pressure had formed at the beginning of a month.

In the mid afternoon of the last day of September, it came. The moving floe pushed fiercely on the port bow under the foremast. On deck, Greenstreet was fixated as the foremast flailed about and appeared to be "coming out of her with the tremendous jerks it gave." Huge beams in the Ritz bowed like saplings. Deck planks and uprights creaked, jumped, and buckled. The *Endurance* quivered throughout, uttering moans, cracks, and bangs. For a frightening hour, the million-ton floe relentlessly bore down on the port bow, and then cracked across about 500 yards from the ship. The pressure ceased. Some deck planks remained buckled and gear was strewn about, but amazingly the *Endurance* was intact.

The next day Wild shot two huge, bull crab-eater seals. The crew feasted on seal liver, a most welcome change in diet. The officers and others in the

Ritz moved back to the deckhouse wardroom. Over the next week the weather warmed to above freezing. The men stripped off their heavy clothing as if it were a summer heat wave. After being acclimated to minus 20°, indeed, it was.

The pack showed signs of opening. Spring was in the air. Seals and penguins were again common, and even whales blew in open water between the floes. On October 14, the floe that had pushed under the *Endurance* in July slipped away. The ship floated in open water, free after 9 months! Two days later Shackleton instructed crew to pump water into the boilers and light the fires to prepare for escape.

A lead appeared the next day; however, fixing a leak in the boiler kept them from using the engine. Under full sail, the ship wouldn't budge, as it was locked in by ice. No leads appeared the next day, and the ice pressure returned. Floes pushed relentlessly on both sides of the ship. Within several seconds, the ice pushed over the *Endurance* and she came to rest, tipped 30 degrees to port. Everything not secured crashed across the decks. Pots emptied their contents onto the fires in the galley. By early evening, the men stowed and tied down everything. An hour later, the pressure subsided and the pack loosened. The floes under the ship pulled apart, and she righted herself.

The next day the barometer read 28.96, the lowest since the July blizzard. Three days later the temperature dropped from 10° to minus 14°. The southwest wind that had brought the cold weather shifted 180 degrees to the northeast, pushing the pack hard against the ship. Two days later, in the early evening of October 24, the ice pressure came as never before. Alexander Macklin, one of the surgeons, wrote: "The whole sensation was of something colossal, of something in nature too big to grasp."

Floes buffeted each other and the ship until the *Endurance* was in a killer squeeze: a floe on starboard side forward, another on starboard aft, and a third amidships port side. A huge chunk of ice plowed across the stern, ripping the stern post that held the rudder partly away from the planking on the starboard side. The sea had gained access—water cascaded down and flowed forward into the engine room. The firemen raised steam to operate the bilge pumps, but the water level continued to rise. The men worked the main hand pumps to no avail—the intake pipe near the keel of the ship was frozen.

Worsley, Greenstreet, and Hubert Hudson, the navigator, descended into the pitch black, freezing-cold bowels of the ship, working their way through tons of coal and slimy seal blubber to reach the intakes. While

Green poured boiling water into the frozen pipe, the men heated fittings with a blow torch and hammered the pipe. After an hour's toil, water flowed. The skilled carpenter, McNeish, worked for 28 hours to construct a coffer-dam 10 feet from the stern to keep the water from flowing forward. Outside, the men used ice saws and picks to cut the ice slabs bearing down on the ship, only to have the loose chunks pushed aside and the onslaught continue.

All night they sawed, axed, and pumped—15 minutes on, 15 off. When a man wasn't working, he sought a few moments rest, only to be called back to duty just as he drifted into sleep. After 10 hours, hardened as they were, the exhausted men staggered as if in a drunken stupor. Shackleton ordered an hour's rest, during which Green served breakfast porridge. McNiesh's cofferdam slowed the flow but they still had to pump. The men prepared dog teams and sledges for a quick departure, and readied the three boats for lowering. At 9 p.m., Shackleton ordered the men to lower the boats. They off-loaded and organized provisions and essentials on what appeared to be a stable floe.

During all this commotion, an unusually large group of 10 emperor penguins emerged from the chaotic piles of ice. Momentarily they stopped, bowed. Then, after giving the tortured *Endurance* never-before-heard, dirge-like utterances, they marched into the night.

The pressure squeeze held. By the afternoon of October 26, decks and bulkheads—the *Endurance* itself—could take no more: beams splintered, decks bowed and broke, the stern pushed up 20 feet, rudder and sternpost ripped away. Water flowed freely forward, and the bow sunk, laden with frozen water. Like robots, the men continued pumping until Shackleton formally acknowledged what they already knew. At 5 p.m., he signaled Wild, who quietly informed two men trying to sleep below: "She's going, boys. I think it's time to get off."

Side Note 4.

- When the *Endurance* was crushed, all knew the situation had changed, but they had a plan to trek to land and rescue.
- In 1988, the hottest year on record at the time, James Hansen testified before the U.S. Senate that his analyses indicated with 99 percent confidence that scientists had confirmed climate warming.
- The global community responded by founding the United Nations Intergovernmental Panel on Climate Change (IPCC).

1.10: The crushed *Endurance* held up by ice that had pierced her hull.

The crew moved their essentials to a floe 100 yards away and pitched tents on the snow. However, before they could settle in, the floe began to crack and break up. The men moved to a sturdier floe some 200 yards distant. They put down canvas and boards as tent floors, but that night there were not enough to go around. A man's body heat will melt the snow, and soon he will be in a pool. However, all that mattered to their exhausted bodies was sleep. So sleep they did, on boards or canvas or snow, piled close together to keep from freezing. Shackleton walked the floe because the pack remained in turmoil.

A little after midnight, Boss felt the ice quake as a crack opened among the tents. He roused the dead-to-the-world *Endurance* Party to move camp to the larger piece of the cracked floe. They slept again while night watch-man Shackleton resumed his walking, contemplating their new situation: "The destruction and abandonment of the ship was no sudden shock. The disaster had been looming ahead for many months, and I had studied my plans for all contingencies a hundred times." His thoughts were less than uplifting, with the men's safety his primary concern:

> I must bend my energies and mental power and apply every bit of knowledge that experience of the Antarctic had given me. The task was likely to be long and strenuous, and an ordered mind and a clear programme were essential if we were to come through without loss of life. A man must shape himself to a new mark directly [when] the old one goes to ground.

CHAPTER 2
Living on the Floes

At dawn, Shackleton, Hurley, and Wild returned to the *Endurance* to secure with some difficulty petrol and tin cans in which to warm milk for the men. They went from tent to tent "with the life-giving drink." The lack of appreciation given by some prompted Wild to say, "If any of you gentlemen would like your boots cleaned just put them outside!"

Painfully, ever so slowly, the camp came to life. In time, each man did his part to sort and stow equipment and to load boats on sledges. During the day, new clothing and sleeping bags were issued. Sleeping bags—18 reindeer bags and 10 less-warm woolen bags—were distributed by lottery. Shackleton, Wild, Worsley, and several other leaders didn't join in. They took the woolen bags. Rank has its privilege, but fairness and a concern for others elicited an allegiance to Boss and the community far deeper than ever possible with more top-down relations.

The men were not discouraged, nor had they internalized the monumental consequences of losing their ship. They had no energy for it. After all, they were alive, and the months of drifting and waiting were over. They had, at last, a meaningful task. Get home to civilization without the *Endurance*.

All knew the plan. Walk northwest across the floes some 350 miles to Paulet Island and the stores left there in 1903—more than a decade earlier—by a rescue ship. The Swedish ship *Antarctic* had been crushed, and the crew over-wintered on the island before being rescued.

The *Endurance*, too, had been crushed but then run through by spears of ice that kept the mangled wreck from sinking. When the pressure eased, the ice withdrew, but until then a disheveled entangled collection of sails, ropes, pipes, broken masts, splintered planks and beams adorned what remained of the hull. This was good fortune—the *Endurance* Party needed all that they could salvage.

In the afternoon of the second day on the ice, Shackleton gathered the beleaguered expedition among the tents to establish the importance of weight. Lansing wrote:

> Each man, he said, would be allowed the clothes on his back, plus two pairs of mittens, six pairs of socks, two pairs of boots, a sleeping bag, a pound of tobacco, and two pounds of personal gear. Speaking with the utmost conviction, Shackleton pointed out that no article was of any value when weighted against their ultimate survival, and he exhorted them to be ruthless in ridding themselves of every unnecessary ounce, regardless of its [presumed] value.

To make his point, he tossed his gold cigarette case, along with several gold coins, into the snow. In his hand was a Bible given to him by Queen Alexandra with her inscription on the flyleaf: "May the Lord help you to do your duty & guide you through all the dangers by land and sea. May you see the Works of the Lord & all His Wonders in the deep." He ripped out the flyleaf, the Twenty-third Psalm, and a page of Job including the verse: "Out of whose womb came the ice? And the hoary frost of Heaven, who hath gendered it? The waters are hid as with a stone. And the face of the deep is frozen." Gently placing the Bible in the snow, Shackleton walked away.

2.1: Shackelton places in the snow the Bible given to him by Queen Alexandra.

The message was clear. The men piled their irrelevant worldly possessions on top of gold and Bible. Leonard Hussey's 12-pound zither banjo, however, was spared—Shackleton knew well music's social glue. The surgeons kept medical supplies and instruments deemed necessary. Hurley retained his small camera and several rolls of film.

On October 30, after 2 days of packing and salvaging from the wreck, the crew left Dump Camp and began the march to Paulet Island. Breaking trail were Shackleton, James Wordie, Hussey, and Hudson, with a sledge carrying shovels and pickaxes to clear the way and build ramps over high-pressure ridges. Next came seven dog-pulled sledges, each with hundreds of pounds of gear, followed by two boats on sledges pulled by 15 men under Worsley's direction. It was 15°, so the snow was wet. Pulling the boats was nearly impossible. Advancing 400 yards at a time was all they could manage. The party stayed close together so as not to be separated if a crack opened. They stopped after 3 hours, just 1 mile from the *Endurance*. Supper was at 6 p.m., then sleep.

The crew awoke to half a foot of new, soggy snow and a blistering 25°. On the move at midday, pulling sledges and boats through a foot of slush, the men were soon sweating profusely. They were thirsty, and there was little to drink. Eating snow directly is a losing proposition. Melting snow in one's mouth takes considerable energy that body heat supplies, which in turn comes from food, a limited resource. Sledges work well at temperatures below zero because the snow is frozen solid and provides minimal friction, but at 25°, it felt like dragging objects through mud. By mid afternoon the men had advanced only three-quarters of a mile. Stranded on the only safe floe in sight, Shackleton called it a day and camped.

2.2: Men hauling the *Caird* across wet snow and ice.

Side Note 5.

- Shackleton's plan to trek to land and rescue failed. It failed because he and his crew could not overcome the forces of nature.
- By 2000, the Intergovernmental Panel on Climate Change had yet to achieve among nations a consensus that climate change was happening or imminent, and that the nations of the world needed to rapidly arrest the human caused release of heat trapping gases. On our current course, climate instability and biological chaos will ensue.
- In both instances physics and biology dictate the outcome.

The next morning, Shackleton, Wild, and Worsley scouted for a route, but the floes to the west were a tangled jumble of pressure ridges and immense slabs of broken ice. Further advancement was impossible. Shackleton decided to move back a mile or so to a sturdy floe and to stay there until they drifted closer to land. Fortunately, the new site, Ocean Camp, was not far from Dump Camp and the wreck, so the crew retrieved many supplies over the coming days.

No longer did the men have the warmth provided by the *Endurance*, so their bodies had to do the heating. That required considerably more food. Shackleton asked Green to add blubber to the seal stew, which rose to the surface as rubbery globs. The men picked them out, just too disgusting to eat. Soon, however, as Worsley noted:

It is scandalous—all we seem to live for and think of now is food. I have never in my life taken half such a keen interest in food as I do now—and we are all alike ... We are ready to eat anything, especially cooked blubber, which none of us would tackle before.

A week earlier, they had been living well on the *Endurance*—dry, in their own beds; with warm, sufficient, and good food; cozy and comfortable in the Ritz with regular entertainment. On the ice they were cold, wet, and hungry; crowded in tents without amenities; sleeping on ice or cold planks; and eating out of aluminum mugs in which everything was mixed, assisted only by spoon, knife, and fingers. Yet, the men were basically content, if not happy. None of the diaries recorded signs of depression or discontent, just the details of the day's events along with mostly positive reflections and an obsession with food.

Salvage parties traveled to Dump Camp and back again to the *Endurance,* from which they brought back all manner of useful things. Seamen Walter How and William Bakewell made a fantastic find—Hurley's cases of photographic negatives, still dry, which they delivered to him. Because of their weight, Shackleton allowed Hurley to keep only 150 glass negatives. McNeish and several others attacked the deck above the Ritz to gain access to food sealed below. After chiseling for several hours, they jury-rigged a block and tackle to rip open a hole in the deck. Out floated several tons of stores: baking soda, barley, flour, jam, lentils, rice, spices, sugar, and vegetables. To celebrate, Green made curried seal for supper. It was almost uneatable. It burned their mouths and gave them an unquenchable thirst. Green had added way too much curry.

A blizzard set in, and the men were tent bound for 2 days. Shackleton took the slack time to assess the food situation with Hurley, Wild, and Worsley: 3 months at full rations, not counting the sledging rations originally for the six-man transcontinental party. They decided full rations would last until January—2 months from then—after which they would have a better idea of their options. It all depended upon drift. Northwest to land, northeast to the open seas of the Drake Passage—the worst seas in the world, or drift could just stop, forcing another winter-over on the ice. Summer would bring an abundance of seals, penguins, and other food to stockpile for the dark, cold, storm-plagued winter. No one, however, wanted to entertain that possibility.

Shackleton invited Hurley to this decision making meeting not because of his Antarctic experience or special knowledge but his own overriding desire to keep everyone working together and avoid strife. Hurley, despite his daring and great physical strength and endurance, had an inherent fear of having a situation spin out of control, a dread that could make him loose confidence and cause dissention in the group. While Shackleton clearly appreciated Hurley's exceptional photography skills, work ethic, and willingness to accomplish tasks at hand, he flattered him in part to satisfy his need to be important. Shackleton assigned Hurley to his own tent to keep an eye on him. He also put Hudson and James with him so they didn't get on the nerves of the others. For similar reasons Shackleton had instructed the expedition's leaders to "keep an eye" on particular men. For example, McNeish, an exceptional carpenter and a well-seasoned sailor, had the tendency to be pugnacious. A stickler for the seaman's rights, he was assigned to Wild's tent.

2.3: Ocean Camp, one of the crew's homes during their 6 months on the ice.

The men settled into Ocean Camp's routine. Each stood a night watch of 1 hour. At 6:30 a.m. the watchman lit fires in the galley, and at 7:45 he went among the tents saying, "Lash up and stow," meaning get up and pack your gear. After breakfast the men worked on various preparations. Mc-Neish and several others spent weeks building up the sides of the two largest boats to make them more seaworthy. Hurley, also a tinsmith, constructed a boat pump and a blubber-fueled cooking stove from scrap metal. Hunting parties were always active. When they killed a seal, the hunters signaled those who were training or exercising the dog teams to come and haul the meat to camp. Hussey would warm his fingers by the galley fire and then play his banjo as the men gathered around to sing. Each tent settled into an evening routine—poker, bridge, and other card games; telling tales; and endless discussions over etiquette or other trivia. The eight men in Worsley's tent read to each other from the few books they had rescued: Clark's copy of *Science from an Easy Chair* and Sir Walter Scott's *Marmion*.

The wind changed from southeast to north, bringing warm weather. The temperature hit a high of 35°. The men shed their clothes and washed with snow. However, the surface became a watery mess and very annoying. A man could step and plunge into slush up to his knee, often his waist. Everybody was always wet, and it became miserably hot inside the tents, where temperatures reached more than 80°.

On November 21, the *Endurance* wreck sank. In his diary, Shackleton simply stated, "I cannot write about it." The sinking was emotional and symbolic. An old, sick friend had gone, leaving them memories, but the tangible connections to the civilization she symbolized were gone. The next night, to everyone's delight, Shackleton called for a special supper, fish paste and biscuits. All were upbeat. Macklin wrote:

> Really, this sort of life has its attractions. I read somewhere that all a man needs to be happy is a full stomach and warmth, and I begin to think it is nearly true. No worries, no trains, no letters to answer, no collars to wear—but I wonder which of us would not jump at the chance to change it all tomorrow!

Despite the minimal materials available, McNeish had masterfully raised the sides of the two boats so they would be ready for the boat trip when the time came. As November ended, the men had done everything they could: they readied the boats, strengthened the sledges and sledging harnesses, and packed and repacked gear. However, in the first weeks of December, Shackleton became tent-bound with a painful bout of sciatica. By mid-month the men were getting restless. The drift had averaged 2 miles per day, but it was mostly north—and land was to the northwest. Spells of warm weather opened leads all around and they practiced launching the boats. Boss believed the ice was breaking up and he worried about the northward drift, but more about morale. He wrote in his diary, "Am thinking of starting off for the west."

On December 20, after conferring with Wild, Shackleton announced they would march to the west to close the distance to Paulet Island. Intense debate ensued. Greenstreet believed, "… the going will be awful, everything being in a state of softness far worse than when we left the ship, and in my opinion it would be a measure to be taken only as a last resort and I sincerely hope he will give up the idea directly." Furthermore, Worsley stated, "My idea is to stay here—unless the drift should become large to the East. … the drift will convey us part of our journey…" Macklin and others sided with Shackleton, "… personally I think that we ought to push west as hard as we can. … drift will take us north, and the resulting direction will be NW, the direction in which we want to go." Three dog teams left the next morning to explore the ice to the west and concluded that westward progress was possible. The crew held a Christmas feast on December 22 and stuffed themselves.

Up at 3:30 a.m. on December 23, the men were moving by 4. Within 3 hours they had sledged the two boats a mile and returned for breakfast. The men harnessed up at 9 to pull sledges loaded with supplies to the boats. Shortly after midday, they pitched tents and everyone slept. At 7 that evening Shackleton asked Worsley to put a bottle with a note in the *Stancomb Wills,* which was back at Ocean Camp. It read: "*Endurance* crushed and abandoned in 69° 5' S and 51° 35' W. All hands to-morrow proceeding to the westward. All well. December 23rd, 1915. E. H. Shackleton."

The note would let the world know what had happened should the crew disappear and the message be found. Shackleton didn't want the men to know for fear they could interpret it as loss of hope.

At 8 p.m. they were off. They had covered only 1½ miles before encountering open water and broken ice. They pitched camp and slept.

The next day offered no safe route—the pack had loosened and presented too much open water. However, by 3 a.m. on Christmas morning, the ice had closed, and the men resumed their trek. The surface was mush—with each step the men's feet would break through, often to their knees or higher. Their leather boots, equipped with a cloth upper that reached the knee, were designed for hard, frozen snow—not slush. With each step, the men had to lift a water-filled boot weighing some 7 pounds a foot or two out of slush, only to sink again with the next step. Walking was exhausting. Pulling a load, no less a 1-ton boat, was beyond belief.

The men struggled on—wet, hungry, thirsty, and tired. On December 27, after covering a mere thousand yards in several hours, McNeish told Worsley he would do no more. Worsley was not a particularly competent leader, and exhausted and frustrated himself, he informed Shackleton. Boss took McNeish aside and, in no uncertain terms, told him it was his duty to follow orders. McNeish responded that his contract was for duty on the *Endurance.* Because the ship was lost, he did not have to obey orders according to established seamen's rights. Shackleton reminded him that a clause in his contract stated, "to perform any duty on board, in the boats, or on shore as directed by the master and owner." McNeish protested. Shackleton walked away. When they resumed pulling the boats, McNeish was at his place.

McNeish's disobedience worried Shackleton. Anarchy was not an option. Before turning in that evening, Shackleton brought the men together and read the contract each had signed.

After another day of exhausting effort, open leads and broken ice made further progress not possible. In 7 days the men had covered just 7½ of the

Side Note 6.

- The second trekking attempt was to be a morale booster and an attempt to get closer to land. It failed on both accounts. It left no doubt that the party was in dire straits.
- In 2012, James Hansen and colleagues published a paper that affirmed a prediction Hansen had made in 1988—in the first decade of the 21st century the climate dice would be loaded for hot temperature extremes. Major climate instability had arrived. Humanity is now in dire straits. We can only lessen the instability, not avoid it.

300 miles to land. With such little progress and the condition of the ice, the decision was obvious. Shackleton wrote:

> Turned in but could not sleep. Thought the whole matter over & decided to retreat to more secure ice: it is the only safe thing to do. … Am anxious: For so big a party & 2 boats in bad conditions we could do nothing: I do not like retreating but prudence demands this course: Everyone working well except carpenter: I shall never forget him in this time of strain & stress.

After rejecting several unsafe sites, the team settled on a flat, heavy floe with somewhat rotten ice, 7-feet thick. Worsley named it Mark Time Camp, as if they would soon again be on the move. After their week of intense activity, the men now had nothing to do but wait. Temperatures remained around 32°, creating an irritating mess of knee-deep and frequently waist-deep slush.

The miserable conditions and passage of time enabled the men to finally fully grasp the reality of their situation. They were not in charge. Escape was at the whim of winds, seas, and weather. Uncertainty becomes particularly unsettling when one accepts that nature and chance hold one's fate. Most people simply believe otherwise. When belief is shaken, things can fall apart. Shackleton knew this and fully accepted his role as leader to ensure the men believed—as did he—that they would persevere.

The men had food for some 40 days at full rations. During the first week of January 1916, they killed a dozen seals, including a 1,100-pound sea leopard that had leapt onto the floe and was about to make a meal of Orde-Lees. Wild downed him with half a dozen shots. Shackleton decided this newly acquired food supply was good for a month and sufficient for

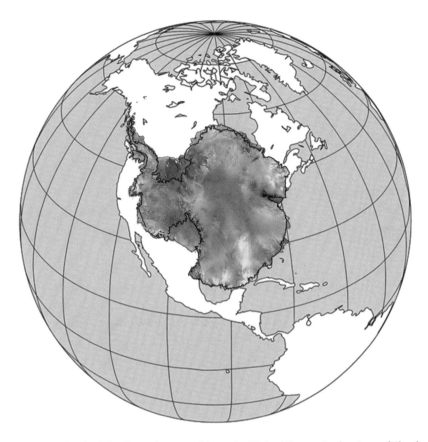

2.4: Antarctica is a big place, almost as big as the United States. At the time of Shackleton's expedition, it had no human infrastructure, no cities, no towns, and no people, just a few huts used infrequently by explorers like Amundsen, Shackleton, and Scott.

the time being, and inexplicably ordered the men not to retrieve three of the killed seals. A number of the men questioned his decision. Shackleton considered this a sign of disloyalty, a questioning of his capacity to lead them out of this morass. Like everybody else, he was stressed, not because of the unpleasant conditions, but because he was responsible for 27 men, and his primary plan had failed. Not getting the seals was a trivial thing, and apparently he recognized his poor decision when he wrote, "I suppose it is the strain. … I long for some rest, free from thought."

The weather continued to deteriorate over the next few days. Temperatures rose to above freezing, with wet snow and rain. The men were tentbound and got on each other's nerves. Some even complained about

Hussey's banjo playing. The month's supply of food was dwindling faster than anticipated. Shackleton considered killing the dogs. Trekking was no longer possible anyway, and it would save food.

The men, who had created deep attachments to their beloved dogs, clearly resented Shackleton for his idea. As Greenstreet wrote:

[T]he present shortage of food, is due simply and solely from the Boss refusing to get seals when they were to be had and even refusing to let Orde-Lees to go out to look for them. … His sublime optimism all the way thro being to my mind absolute foolishness. Everything right away thro was going to turn out all right and no notice was taken of things possibly turning out otherwise and here we are.

By mid-January, the ice at Mark Time Camp had so deteriorated that the team had moved 150 yards away to a more stable floe, dubbing it Patience Camp. Shackleton quietly ordered Wild to shoot all the dogs except Hurley and Macklin's teams, which he sent back to Ocean Camp for supplies. The 9-hour trip was horrendous, but the men returned with 1,000 pounds of canned meat and vegetables, tapioca, dog pemmican, jam, and dry milk.

A few days later, on January 16, the wind shifted to the southwest and picked up. A gale blew for 6 days, pushing the men 84 miles north and across the Antarctic Circle. This storm had also blown Ocean Camp to within 5 miles

2.5: Dog sledding, an invaluable service, also provided entertainment. By caring for the dogs the men created companionships that nurtured health and well being of both men and dogs.

of their current position. With no open water between the two camps, the dog teams again trekked to Ocean Camp on January 30, retrieving 60 pounds of bouillon cubes, an abundance of tobacco, and several books, including some volumes of the *Encyclopedia Britannica*. A few days later, on Worsley's persistent encouragement, Shackleton sent Worsley and 18 men to retrieve the *Stancomb Wills*. Several hours after their return, Shackleton asked Macklin to take his team back for another load of supplies. Two miles from their destination, however, the men encountered open water and had to turn back. Luck had been with them in getting the third boat on the first trip—that was the last time Ocean Camp would be accessible.

Everyone looked forward to Shackleton's birthday on February 15, for it might mean a good meal, if not a feast. The food supply, however, was diminishing. More problematic was a mere 10-day supply of blubber for cooking. The men dug up discarded seal heads and flippers to scavenge more blubber. The monotony of waiting was affecting everyone. Not only were the men bored, but they had almost nothing to eat except meat—seal and penguin. Supplies, too, were low: milk, tea, and flour were nearly gone, and the cocoa was spent. The men starved by trying to stay warm. They had to move about and exercise to keep warm—this created a dilemma. Be warm and painfully hungry or be cold and just hungry. If a man crawled into his wet, frigid, often frozen sleeping bag, he was too cold to sleep. If he exercised sufficiently to be warm, he was too hungry to sleep.

Several times a day, Worsley climbed a small berg on the flow to look west for land. He reported seeing the possible reflection of Mount Haddington in the sky, but the men were too cautious to believe him. Shackleton knew a change was needed. Since 1916 was a leap year, he celebrated February 29 with a "Bachelor's Feast." Greenstreet wrote in his diary, "For the first time in many days, I have finished a meal without wanting to start all over again."

Paulet Island was becoming an impossible destination. It lay 91 miles west-northwest, and the camp was drifting north. Snowstorms confined the men to their tents, and temperatures dropped below zero by nighttime. With groups of four to eight men penned up in the tiny, cold, wet, smelly tents, even the littlest things created friction. In one tent, Clark's constant sniffling annoyed some during the day and kept others awake at night. Orde-Lees and Blackborow's intense snoring became intolerable. There was no escape from Worsley and Orde-Lees' constant chatter and argument over trivia. The men were held hostage in a life without meaning. Greenstreet wrote:

Day passes day with very little or nothing to relieve the monotony. We take constitutionals round and round the floe but no one can go further as we are, to all intents and purposes, on an island. There is practically nothing fresh to read and nothing to talk about, all topics being absolutely exhausted.

Then it happened. On March 9, for the first time in more than a year, the men felt the ocean's swell. Excitedly, they pointed out to each other the gentle rise and fall of neighboring floes, as waves undulated through the pack. How far was the open ocean? Worsley timed the rise and fall. The men agreed that open water could be no further than 30 miles. However, Shackleton was concerned. The action of the sea would break the ice sheets to pieces. They would have no floe to camp on, and if leads didn't open, colliding chunks of ice would smash the boats to pieces.

The next morning, the swell was gone, the ice packed tightly once again. Spirits plummeted. Escape was not at hand. Shackleton ordered an afternoon drill to test how quickly the men could remove the boats from sledges and load them if their floe broke apart. The men followed orders, but tempers flared. They exchanged harsh words. The drill revealed to all the reality of the diminished supplies. A cold, southerly gale blew in, blasting more snow. No one spoke as they retired to their tents. The disappointment of the morning slipped into a deepening sense of desperation.

The men ate the last of their flour. Tea and coffee were gone, too. Blubber for cooking was in such short supply that seal steaks were dropped from breakfast, and drinking water, which they had to melt from ice, was no more. If a man wanted water, he melted snow in a tin container by holding it against his body. However, the yield was small—just a spoonful or two. The men received only one hot drink each day—a mug of diluted milk at breakfast.

An insatiable craving for food gnawed at body and mind. Frustration and blame simmered about Shackleton's failure to stockpile seals when they were in abundance and to retrieve all the stores at Ocean Camp when it was possible. Storekeeper Orde-Lees broached the food issue with Shackleton, who harshly responded, "It will do some of these people good to go hungry; their bloody appetites are too big!" For entertainment, Greenstreet and Worsley discussed eating Marston, because he was the plumpest among them. They offered him chewed bones, telling him not to get too thin. They debated who would get the best body parts. Marston avoided them like the plague.

Often constipated because of their all-meat diet, the men used snow or ice in lieu of toilet paper, which chafed their already sore behinds. Eyes watered constantly, causing runny noses that developed open sores. Their sleeping bags and clothes were filthy and in a constant state of damp to soaking wet. The men never removed their underwear. Faces and hands were blackened from blubber smoke, and they stank. There was nothing to do but pass the time cursing the wind, the snow, the lack of food, and each other on the slightest provocation.

Early in the morning of March 23, 1916, Shackleton spotted land. Running among the tents he yelled, "Land in sight! Land in sight!" A few came out to look, but others were skeptical and stayed in the sack, thinking it another false sighting of an iceberg. But this *was* land—one of the Danger Islets 42 miles away. Twenty miles further west was Paulet Island. This original destination was unreachable, however—travel across the pack wasn't possible, and the boats were useless in the tightly packed ice.

The next day dawned beautifully clear to reveal Joinville Island at the very end of Palmer Peninsula, 57 miles due west. However, as the men drifted more miles north each day, making the peninsula less and less reachable, they became anxious. At 120 miles due north lay the only land that separated them from sure death in the open ocean of the Drake Passage: Clarence and Elephant islands.

During the evening of March 28, the men again felt a gentle ocean swell. By dawn the swell was more substantial, splitting their floe and separating the boats and tents from their store of meat. The night watchman shouted, "Crack! Lash up and stow!" The men literally leapt from their tents. Quickly, they tossed the meat across the opening crack and moved the *Caird* to the floe's center. However, as breakfast began, the floe cracked under the boat. Dropping their mugs, the men ran to pull it closer to the tents. Suddenly, out of the mist, a large animal appeared. Wild grabbed his rifle and fired a shot. An 11-foot, 1,000-pound sea leopard lay dead. Food at last and blubber for 2 weeks! In the seal's gut they found 50 newly caught fish, an unexpected treat they enjoyed the next day. Lunch that day was a feast of sea leopard liver—the men's first hot lunch in week.

The men spotted jellyfish in the open water between floes. They also saw cape pigeons, terns, a giant petrel, and a black water sky to the northwest—all signs of open water. The temperature reached 34°. That afternoon, the swell was so great that Shackleton decided they should be ready to launch the boats. He commenced two watch teams: 4 hours on, 4 hours off. The men's spirits soared.

However, the pack changed little over the next day. Shackleton reinstated a single watchman because a breakup of the ice didn't appear imminent. That evening, after everyone had turned in, a big swell cracked the floe a few feet from Wild's tent. The watchman shouted, "Crack!" Confusion reigned in the cold, dark night as the men struggled to put on their frozen boots and move the boats and supplies away from the crack. Shackleton reset sea watches and told the men to turn in fully dressed. Few men slept as their floe banged against neighboring floes and pitched up and down in the heavy swell.

Worsley took a sighting the following day, March 31, establishing that they had drifted 28 miles north in the past 6 days. Worsley was astonished. The wind had been out of the north, yet they were drifting north. Strong currents were pushing the pack due north against the wind. The wind died down that afternoon, and the swell vanished. By the next sighting, on April 5, they were 21 miles west, this time moving against westerly winds. This was very bad news. If this westerly drift persisted, it would push their floe between King George Island and Elephant Island out into the Drake Passage, a place of no return. At noon the next day, Worsley took another sighting. They had moved 8 miles due north and glimpsed Clarence and Elephant islands. By April 7, they had drifted 18 miles almost due east. Fickle currents were pushing them north, then west, north again, and then east.

The seas and ice were in chaotic turmoil. Every time their jostled home bumped or crashed into another floe, ice broke off, thereby reducing their island's size and stability. More problematic were 3-foot waves coming from the northwest. That night, an unusually high wave lifted their floe so high that its two ends were relatively unsupported. The floe cracked in half, right underneath the *Caird*. On watch, Worsley shouted for help. Scrambling from their tents, the men rescued the *Caird* and then the other boats from the broken-off piece. Their drifting home, formerly larger than a square mile, had been reduced to one percent of its original size, a small triangle of 90 by 100 by 120 yards. Macklin summed up the mood, "[we want to] be off this drifting uncontrollable pack, taking us we know not where, and in spite of any efforts we may attempt to make … and puny mortals that we are, can do nothing to help ourselves against these colossal forces of nature."

On their ever-shrinking ice raft, the men were an odd addition to the abundant sea life. Penguins and seals frolicked in the water and on ice. Skua gulls and snow and giant petrels soared above, while large fleas hopped across the water. Whales—dreaded killer whales among them—blew everywhere. Often more than 25 feet long, these voracious predators sport a mouth capable of opening to 4 feet wide. Killer whales were known to leap onto or break a floe to engulf an inattentive seal. Tales have been told of them capsizing a boat and feasting on the crew.

Everybody was on edge. Land was in sight, but unattainable. Their days on the floes were numbered, but there was no escape. To launch boats into the tumultuous ocean of closely packed floes would be suicide. To remain camped on a chunk of ice that was disintegrating beneath their feet was just another way to die. Ever optimistic, Shackleton wrote:

> I confess that I felt the burden of responsibility sit heavily on my shoulders; but, on the other hand, I was stimulated and cheered by the attitude of the men. Loneliness is the penalty of leadership, but the man who has to make the decisions is assisted greatly if he feels that there is no uncertainty in the minds of those who follow him, and that his orders will be carried out confidently and in expectation of success.

The men watched and waited. A little past midnight on April 9 the ice opened, only to close at 5 a.m., opened again at 8 and closed at 9. Wave height increased. Floes slammed into each other. The ice opened again at 9:30. An hour later, Shackleton's voice rang out, "Strike the tents and clear the boats!" In minutes, the men dismantled the tents, stowed gear, and pushed boats on sledges to the water's edge. Minutes later the floe split, right where the tents had stood, to separate the *Wills* from a substantial pile of supplies. As the halves drifted apart, men jumped across the open water between the fractured floe and quickly shuttled the *Wills* and stores onto what remained of Patience Camp. They waited and wondered—go or stay? Green, ever mindful of his role, had made seal soup and hot powdered milk for lunch. All watched Shackleton. He watched the ice and sea. Patience Camp was but 50 yards across. "Launch the boats." It was 12:40 p.m. The *Docker*, *Wills*, and *Caird* went into the water. One by one they were loaded, and within an hour, as the pack began to close once again, the men rowed for open water.

CHAPTER 3

Reaching Land

The men hadn't exercised much over the previous several months and hadn't rowed at all for almost 2 years. Their oars awkwardly hit the ice and each other. The raised sides on the *Docker* and *Caird* hindered proper oar placement, and the men used boxes of supplies on the seats to raise the rowers' positions to make rowing possible. For an hour they worked the boats through small channels of open water until finally entering an expanse of unobstructed water. They steered northwest. Suddenly, a low rumbling noise from the east caught their attention. A 2-foot-high, foaming agglomeration of ice and water was roaring toward them. Totally startled by the rip tide, Shackleton watched in disbelief. Quickly grasping the danger, he turned west, putting the on-coming wall of water astern. The other boats followed suit. For 15 harrowing minutes, the men rowed with every ounce of strength they could muster to keep the boats from being swamped. Facing the stern, the rowers looked at eye level into the churning mass of broken ice as it closed in on them. Those not rowing counted cadence—"stroke, stroke, stroke …"—and urged superhuman efforts. Then it was over. The wave had petered out.

A southwest wind blew as the boats resumed a northwest heading. In the lead was the *James Caird*: 22 feet 6 inches long, 6 feet wide at the beam, 3 feet 7 inches deep, 3¾ tons capacity, two masts for a main and a mizzen sail along with a jib in the bow—all built to Worsley's specifications. With Shackleton as captain, the *Caird* carried Wild, John Vincent, Timothy McCarthy, Hurley, Clark, McNeish, James, Wordie, Hussey, and Green. Next came the *Dudley Docker*, the fastest of the three boats: 22 feet long, a 6-foot beam, 3 feet deep, 1½ ton capacity, one mast for a single lug sail, and Norway-made for hunting bottlenose whales. Worsley was captain of the *Docker*, which carried Greenstreet, Cheetham, Macklin, Thomas McLeod, Marston, Kerr, Orde-Lees, and Holness. Bringing up the rear was the *Stancomb Wills*:

20 feet 8 inches long with a 5-foot-6-inch beam, 2 feet 3½ inches deep, 1¼ ton capacity, one mast for a small mainsail and jib, and also Norway-made for hunting bottlenose whales. Hudson was captain, with the *Wills* carrying Crean, How, Bakewell, James McIlroy, Blackborow, and Stevenson.

The men were sailing in the Bransfield Strait that bridges the gap between the Weddell Sea and the Drake Passage. Discovered in 1820 by Edward Bransfield, few explorers or sailors had been there since, and little was known about the strait then. Today we know that cross seas—wind one way, current another—are common and often produce 2-to-10-foot-high irregularities, or rip tides, that are treacherous for small boats. Skies are clear only 10 percent of the time. Snow and gales are common beginning in February and worsen as winter sets in. Shackleton had good lifeboats, but no type of open boat is suited for the seas and weather of the Bransfield Strait.

That afternoon the men found a flat, wide floe for camp. It took nearly an hour to maneuver the boats and gear onto the ice. Worsley estimated that they had progressed 7 miles northwest. After eating, they went to bed. Shackleton was uneasy. A little before midnight he rose to assess the situation. Shortly thereafter the floe split under his feet and directly under a tent that was housing eight men. As the crack opened, all but one scrambled out. Pulling the tent away, Shackleton saw a moving shape in the water. Quickly, he knelt and yanked out a sleeping bag containing seaman Holness moments before the crack closed.

The ice opened again separating the men in Shackleton's tent and the *Caird* from the rest of the party. The men tossed a line over and pulled the floe pieces close. They hauled the *Caird* across followed by the men. Shackleton held the rope waiting for the last man to cross when the floe crack widened leaving Shackleton alone, unable to hold the ice together. As he drifted out of sight, Shackleton shouted, "Launch a boat!", but Wild had already sent the *Wills* into the night as killer whales blew in the water around the floes. Cuing on Shackleton's voice, they brought him back. Sleep was impossible.

Ice packed around them throughout the night, but by 8 in the morning it had cleared enough to launch boats. At 10 they were again in open water with sails set. Soon they came to a long line of ancient ice and after an hour found a way through, rowing into the open ocean. Biting winds and heavy seas bore directly down as they steered north-northeast. Some men became seasick, but the others ate a hearty lunch. They then sailed and rowed on into a frigid wind and freezing spray. All were tired and miserably cold, yet no one complained, for dozens of miles to the north was what they had dreamed of for nearly a year: land! The boats, however, were rapidly taking on water. Shackleton realized they couldn't continue. Coming about, the fierce winds quickly blew them back to the line of pack ice and they decided to take shelter behind a floe-berg, which in places was 15 feet tall, some 80 feet into the water, and a bit over 100 feet square.

They didn't want to camp on this ice, but conditions allowed no other option. The men required sleep and remaining in the boats was too dangerous. With great effort they hauled the boats and supplies onto the floe-berg, but in the process one man fell in, with Shackleton, Wild, and Hurley almost following. The men were dealing with blistered, frostbitten hands and soaking wet clothes and sleeping bags. Despite their miserable circumstances, they ate a hearty dinner before collapsing with exhaustion into deep sleep.

While they slept, the current and easterly winds blew them west. Dawn, however, revealed tightly packed ancient floes and bergs littering the sea to the horizon. From the northwest, huge, half-mile-long waves rolled through the pack, rhythmically lifting them some 30 feet only to drop them back into a valley surrounded by chaotic, turbulent ice and spray. The floe-berg's depth retarded its drift compared to that of smaller pieces of ice that unrelentingly crashed against their refuge. Howling, gale-force winds and the

3.1: Camping on a floe-berg in the Bransfield Strait during the boat journey to Elephant Island.

noise of grinding, colliding ice filled the air. Their floe-berg was dismantling immediately under their feet. The scene was spectacularly beautiful, if not sublime, yet each man knew his life floated precariously on a dwindling chunk of ice that might split or upend at any moment.

They ate breakfast, packed and stowed, then waited—1 hour, 2 hours, 3 hours. Shackleton stood on a high point, watching the sea and announcing periodically, "A chance is coming," but then, "No." McNeish was standing near an edge when it split off—he quickly jumped across the gap. A bit later, a 20-foot-wide piece of the surface was knocked off at the water line, leaving a shelf across which waves rushed to eat away at the ice above—it appeared that the top half would be sheered off horizontally! The swells grew higher. Anxiety prevailed as the men nervously joked about being dumped off their precarious perch. The waiting continued. 1 p.m. 2 p.m. Darkness would arrive at 5.

Shackleton was watching a lead of open water approaching from the north. To the south, someone observed the unexpected: the 80-foot draft of their floe-berg had apparently deflected a current that was clearing ice to the south. "Launch the boats!" Shackleton shouted as he hurried down from his lookout. In no time, the men were rowing into the center of the open pool in search of a way into the next pool. Then, for no apparent reason, the pack dispersed to create open water all around.

Over the past 2 days, a northeast wind had blown them west. The best open water lay southwest toward King George Island, at that point some 80 miles distant. Clarence or Elephant islands had been their destinations because they were the closest, but ships never sailed near these islands, making rescue unlikely. From King George Island they could island hop to Deception Island, whose excellent harbor whalers routinely visited. Shackleton decided to take advantage of the northeast winds. Hoisting sail, they headed southwest for King George Island.

Under sail, the *Caird* and *Docker* were similarly matched, but the *Wills* soon lagged far behind. Wanting to keep boats together, Shackleton took shelter in the lee of a floe and instructed Worsley to take the *Docker* back for the *Wills*. It was almost dark by the time they returned. They docked at a floe where Green had set up his galley and fixed a hot dinner of seal hoosh—fresh seal meat added to a prepared mixture of beef protein, lard, oatmeal, sugar, salt, and warm milk—that Green passed to the men in the boats. Not wanting to repeat their "floe-berg" nightmare, the men roped the boats together, with *Docker* in the lead. They rowed on a southwest course throughout the night. Snow fell. The temperature was 7°. Rowing was the only way to keep warm. Each man did his turn before huddling with his boat mates, having no place to lie down.

The sun rose into a cloudless sky, providing some relief for their tired, nearly frozen bodies. Green set up his galley on a floe to fix another breakfast of seal hoosh and hot milk. They shoved off, heading southwest on a perfect sailing day. Worsley took sightings at mid-morning and at noon to get two lines necessary to fix their position. He did the calculations twice—then redid them. He was stunned! Their location was 124 miles east of King George Island and 61 miles southeast of Clarence Island. Since leaving Patience Camp they had traveled 22 miles away from land. Their actual location was 50 miles distant from what Worsley expected it to be! One of Bransfield Strait's uncharted currents had taken them back against the winds that they believed were blowing them west toward land.

Shortly after Worsley had secured his second sighting, Shackleton brought the *Caird* alongside the *Docker* and jumped across. Anxiously, he asked Worsley how far they had come. Quietly Worsley conveyed, "30 miles astern, sir." It was very bad news, so Shackleton informed the men, "We haven't done as well as we expected."

Reaching King George Island had become out of the question. After consulting with Wild and Worsley, Shackleton headed south toward Hope Bay at the end of the Palmer Peninsula, some 130 miles distant. The floes were too small to use for fixing dinner that evening, so they ate in the boats. After attempting to moor to a small floe and 3 hectic hours of poling away ice, the men again roped the boats in a line, with *Docker* in the lead. Because of threatening ice, those in the *Docker* rowed just enough to keep the boats in a line and thereby separated. Snow fell and the temperature dropped to minus 4°, freezing their clothes stiff. Staying warm was hopeless. The men huddled together and shivered the minutes away waiting for dawn.

First light revealed a dreadful scene of drained, hollow faces. Everyone was still alive—though barely, by the looks of some. At sunrise the wind shifted to the southeast. Shackleton motioned to Worsley, who brought the *Docker* alongside the *Caird* to confer. For a third time in so many days, they changed plans. Elephant Island, some 100 miles distant, was again their best chance, but only if the southeast wind held.

Shackleton had the remaining stores split up so that each boat had its share in case it became separated. After chipping off ice that had accumulated during the night, the men set sail, the *Caird* in the lead. They maneuvered through broken ice but when the *Caird* collided with a large chunk that put a hole in her bow above the water line, they slowed. Green prepared a hot meal. Shackleton allowed the men to eat all they wanted, although some were too sea sick to partake. For the rest, such a meal revived their dead-tired bodies and flagging spirits.

As noon approached, the pack thinned, allowing them entrance to the open ocean once again. A fierce northwest swell hit hard just as a strong southwest gale caught their sails. Consequently, they were driven up, up, up half-mile hills of water to chaotic tops of tortured water and wind. Then down, down, down the other side—repeatedly, without relief. Periodically, the men lost sight of each other behind the sloping walls of waves. The three small boats were alone in a vast ocean with but two options—Elephant Island or a quick, cold death. Neither was desirable. Either way the odds for survival were about nil.

The gale was so strong that Shackleton ordered twice to trim more sail. *Docker* and *Wills* were taking on water so fast that bailing was almost continuous. Night arrived, and despite Worsley's strong desire to keep sailing, or at least rowing, Shackleton refused. He wanted to keep the boats together for many reasons, but primarily in order to employ Worsley's superior navigational skills. The *Docker* dropped a sea anchor—three oars tied together with canvas around them—with the *Caird* roped to her and the *Wills* to the *Caird*.

The temperature was so low that night that the water breaking over the boats froze on contact. Ankle-deep, ice-cold water soaked the men's feet and forced them to constantly move their toes to keep them from freezing. Lack of pain meant frostbite. Seaman Blackborow had chosen to wear his leather boots despite the others' advice to the contrary. His feet lost feeling. They were so severely frozen that his toes on one foot would later be amputated on a desolate Elephant Island beach. The men cursed everything: a wave that drenched them, their frozen clothing, a bump from a boat mate, their frostbitten cracked lips, and attempts to eat—thirst-parched throats made eating difficult at best.

Despite the circumstances, some of the party managed to maintain a sense of humor. Throughout the night Shackleton asked how they were doing. On one occasion Marston shouted across from the *Docker*, "All right, but I'd like some dry mitts." Shackleton responded, "I left a pair at home. You can have them if you'll drop in and tell 'em I'm coming." Any excuse for a laugh, even at bad humor. Not so humorous was their need to urinate frequently, and many had diarrhea from their high protein diet. To relieve themselves, they had to move to the side of the boat or sit on the frozen gunwale, their naked, sore behinds splashed with icy sea water. The boats iced up quickly. Every 30 minutes the men had to chip it off.

A crystal clear sky on the morning of April 14 inspired them. Hope returned. The peaks of Clarence Island jutted from the horizon to the east, and Elephant Island appeared ahead 30 miles, exactly where Worsley's dead reckoning—distance traveled and direction steered by compass correcting for currents and wind—had predicted. They were, nevertheless, a bedraggled lot. Many of the men had frostbitten faces and broken saltwater boils that oozed a gray gloppy fluid. Blackborow's feet had no feeling. It was impossible to revive circulation. The men were totally spent: exhausted, hungry, and thirsty beyond words.

It took the men more than an hour to chip off the heavy coat of ice that weighted down the boats and bring in the sea anchor. Seaman Holness had two teeth knocked out in the process. Breakfast was nut food and biscuits, but because of the men's extreme thirst, many had to chew on raw, frozen seal meat, which provided a liquid—blood—to coat their throats and help them swallow. By 7 a.m., they were rowing. By 2 p.m. they were just 10 miles from Elephant Island. Adrenaline surged. They would be on land by nightfall! However, over the next hour, despite sailing and rowing as hard as they could, the men made no progress against a strong offshore current. They roped the boats together, with *Docker* in the lead, but to no avail. They cut the *Docker* free, but Shackleton kept the *Wills* in *Caird's* tow. It would be impossible for the *Wills* to stay with the other boats under the existing conditions.

Over the next 2 hours, the wind shifted several times, requiring the men to repeatedly drop and hoist sails. Still, there was no progress. Finally, in the late afternoon, the wind subsided. The men rowed toward a large bay on the southeast side of Elephant Island, hoping for calmer seas and a suitable landing place. Unfortunately, within an hour, a 50-mile-per-hour gale came in from the west-southwest. On Worsley's insistence, Shackleton permitted the *Docker* to proceed alone, but to stay in sight. The men mustered all possible effort to reach land, but the wind and current prevailed. Shackleton abandoned the plan to land on the southeast side of the island in favor of rounding it to find calmer waters.

Around midnight, the *Docker* became swallowed up in a snow squall. When it cleared, Worsley could no longer see the *Caird* and *Wills*. Shackleton, who simultaneously lost sight of the *Docker,* immediately signaled with a candle held against a sail in order to cast the light further into the night. Worsley saw the light and responded, but Shackleton missed his signal. Just then *Docker* became caught in a huge rip tide—waves came over every side: bow, amidships, stern. The crew bailed water furiously. To steady the boat, Worsley ordered the sail lowered and came close to throwing some stores overboard.

Stabilizing the boat was all the exhausted crew could do. Again raising the sail, they headed into the wind, but the *Docker* was sinking from incoming water. Orde-Lees, who until now had refused to row or bail, suddenly realized the gravity of the situation. He found a pot and joined the others, bailing so vigorously that he vomited. Ever so slowly, the *Docker* gained buoyancy, and the crisis passed.

These intense hours drained what energy Worsley had left—his eyes could no longer judge distance, and he nodded off. Macklin offered to take over, but Worsley was unable to move. Positioned at the tiller for almost 4 days, his body had locked in one position. McLeod and Marston dragged him forward over cases and seats, laid him down, and began rubbing his legs and stomach. Finally, Worsley's muscles loosened enough to allow them to stretch out his sleeping body under a tent canvas in the bottom of the boat.

The wild night was made all the worse by the men not knowing where they were. *Docker's* compass had failed, forcing them to rely on Worsley's pocket compass. To obtain a reading, two men hunched under a canvas. One struck a match while the other held the compass. They knew they had to keep a southwest course to avoid what would be a fatal trip through the 14-mile separation between Clarence and Elephant islands into the Drake Passage.

The first rays of dawn revealed a chaotic sea, but dead ahead, less than a mile away, the sheer cliffs of Elephant Island rose in the mist. Relief was short lived, however. A several-foot-high wave suddenly came at them from the cliffs. Greenstreet dropped sail, and the men rowed toward the oncoming wave. A 6-foot wave appeared. Somebody yelled, "Wake the Skipper!" The men uncovered Worsley and shook him. No response. Thinking him dead, Cheetham asked Dr. Macklin for help. He was alive. McLeod kicked him on the back of the head. Nothing, so he kicked again. Worsley stirred and opened his eyes. Startled by the severity of the situation, he yelled, "For God's sake get her around—get away from it! Hoist sail!" The boat was caught in a "williwaw" in which inland storms send 100-mile-per-hour winds down the cliffs to hit the water with enough force to launch tumultuous waves and wind seaward.

Docker came about. The sail caught the wind just as the first wave passed over the stern, nearly knocking Greenstreet off his seat. The second wave swamped *Docker* to half full. The men frantically bailed with pots, mugs, and hands. Slowly, they emptied the boat, and Worsley headed her north to run with the southwest gale. They rounded the northeast end of Elephant Island and sailed down the west side looking for a landing place. For some 14 miles, Worsley sailed west-southwest, past steep cliffs and glaciers with no landing places. Worsley wrote what happened:

> Then I saw a low rocky beach that promised an escape from the sea. For a moment we were amazed by the sight of two small masts. Then we realized that they belonged to our boats, and our amazement changed to joy. They were making into the landing just ahead of us. We gave them three cheers. We landed twenty minutes later.

This new refuge was Cape Valentine at the northeast end of Elephant Island.

The previous night had been similarly miserable on the *Caird* and much worse for *Wills*, which was roped astern of the *Caird*. The same southwest gale had blown the boats to the northeast end of Elephant Island. In the

3.2: The men of the *Endurance* Party were the first people ever to land on Elephant Island, an inhospitable, storm-battered refuge.

morning, they had sailed down the west coast to find the landing place just half an hour ahead of Worsley. Shackleton had maneuvered the *Wills* over the reef and was first to reach the beach. Because no one had ever landed on Elephant Island, Shackleton decided that Blackborow, the youngest in the group, should have the honor. The seaman, however, was listless. In his excitement, Shackleton lifted him over the side, whereupon the young sailor fell into the surf, his frostbitten feet unresponsive. Realizing his mistake, Shackleton jumped overboard and with several others carried the miserable, half-dead seaman onto the beach. As they pulled the boats out of the surf, Rickinson had a mild heart attack that curtailed his usefulness.

CHAPTER 4

Sailing the Drake Passage

After 497 days, the Weddell Sea Party was again on land—a godforsaken spit of a beach 100 feet wide and 50 feet deep. The men walked like drunks. Dazed and shivering they mumbled and aimlessly kicked stones or picked up pebbles and dribbled them through their fingers. The sun momentarily appeared, revealing their hollow white faces. Green served hot milk. The cliffs behind them rose steeply 800 feet to a shallow flat and then up another 2,500 feet. They saw life everywhere: ringed and gentoo penguins, skua gulls, paddies, cormorants, cape pigeons, and seals. They drank their milk in silence, all lost in thought.

The men had quenched their thirst by sucking on glacial ice they had picked up while sailing along the west coast searching for a landing place, but their exhausted, famished bodies needed food. They killed four seals that they immediately butchered. Green fried seal steaks with the fresh supply of blubber. The men then returned to making camp. Green prepared a second batch of steaks which the men quickly consumed. The pattern continued until mid-afternoon. Then they slept. Shackleton and Wild hadn't slept in 4 days—100 hours; the same was true for Greenstreet and Worsley—minus a few hours the night before. James wrote, "Turned in and slept, as we had never slept before, absolute dead dreamless sleep, oblivious of wet sleeping bags, lulled by croaking of the penguins."

No one stirred until midmorning the next day, April 16. After breakfast, the rumor became reality—they were moving. On arrival Wild, Hurley, and Worsley had walked the beach and determined that their camp was just 4 feet above high tide. The cliffs behind them showed storm damage, indicating that they would be swept to sea by the first big storm. Shackleton dispatched Wild in the *Wills* with five men to sail west along the coast to find a safe refuge. The others mostly rested as they were in bad shape from the boat ordeal. Blackborow and Rickinson were incapacitated. Greenstreet could barely walk with his frostbitten feet.

Night came and the men turned in, but with no sign of Wild. The fire in the blubber stove cast its light to sea. Shackleton waited. Shortly afterwards, the *Wills* came out of the night with news. This was a very desolate, unfriendly place. Among the miles of coastline, Wild had located but one suitable spot—about 7 miles down—with a sheltered beach, 150 by 30 yards. A nearby glacier would provide water, and for the moment, penguins, seals, and sea elephants were abundant. Shackleton decided they would leave in the morning.

The men were up at 5 and could see pack ice to the northwest moving toward them. They were so tired and weak that launching the boats proved difficult, almost beyond their strength. The men broke three oars when they used them as rollers. This was bad, because it left the *Wills* with only three oars. Around 11, the tide rose enough to lift the boats over the reef. After 2 miles, they were hit by a williwaw, and then the weather degenerated. Gale to hurricane-force winds blew off the cliffs, making the seas treacherous. The *Wills* couldn't sail, and with just three oars, she began to fall back. Worsley gave an oar to Crean in the *Wills*, leaving *Docker's* crew with three. By early afternoon, they were halfway and took shelter in the lee of a large rock to eat lunch.

Shortly afterwards, the wind swept Worsley's boat seaward toward a 1,000-foot-tall rock pillar some 200 yards offshore. With only three oars, it was nearly blown out to sea, but by using a broken oar and mounting a 2-hour Herculean effort, the crew made it around the rock and closer to land. The *Wills* and the *Caird*, meanwhile, had reached the campsite, where Shackleton was anxiously awaiting the *Docker*. As darkness fell, she appeared, with Greenstreet literally falling out of the boat upon landing. He hobbled on his badly frostbitten feet toward a seal that the men were butchering and thrust his frozen hands into its steaming guts. Greenstreet had loaned his mittens to Clark the day before, and in the rush to leave camp, didn't retrieve them.

No one would wish Elephant Island upon anyone, except perhaps as a place to do penance for the worst of crimes committed by those beyond reform. Soon after arriving at their new site, Macklin wrote: "A more inhospitable place could scarcely be imagined. The gusts increased in violence and became so strong that we could hardly walk against them, and there was not a lee or a scrap of shelter anywhere." The wind tore two of the tents into shreds as the men assembled them. Because the tents were useless now as shelter, the men wrapped themselves in the remnants before sliding into their wet sleeping bags. By morning, a foot of new snow covered everything.

The blizzard persisted, keeping almost everyone in their sleeping bags. The men had no other defense against the wind-propelled snow and ice. Late in the morning, Shackleton ordered the men out to kill penguins. The penguins warmed the men's frostbitten hands as they butchered 77 of about 200 in the nearby rookery.

The nasty weather continued as the men contemplated their situation. They were the first men to ever set foot on this island. Ships never passed. If timber were available, McNeish could have built a boat. Of their three boats, only the *Caird* was even close to seaworthiness. Shackleton told the men what they'd already surmised. When the *Caird* was ready, he and five others would sail for help.

The party had discussed a boat voyage since they'd left Patience Camp. The only uncertainty was the destination. They had three choices: Cape Horn and the island of Tierra del Fuego, 500 miles to the northwest; the Falkland Islands, 500 miles to the north; and South Georgia, 800 miles to the northeast. The dreaded Drake Passage to the north, with its northeast current of 60 miles per day and constant gales in the same direction, made the two closest destinations unattainable. Although the chances of reaching South Georgia were next to none, everyone wanted to attempt it. Over-wintering on Elephant Island—where they had a good chance of dying—was anything but inviting.

Shackleton had pondered the boat crew for months. Wild, the second in command and his trusted friend, would remain on the island to increase the chances that those left behind would survive. The Drake Passage has the worse sailing conditions on Earth. The sun rarely shines, making navigational sightings scarce. Yet the crew would need to sail some 800 miles and intercept a target less than 25 miles wide with little room for error. The trip would be unthinkable without Worsley's navigational skills—he would go. Shackleton also wanted McCarty. He was an experienced sailor, solidly built, never caused any trouble, and among the most likable in the party.

Shackleton selected the other three for mixed reasons. He did not want to leave Crean, because his undiplomatic and offending blunt behavior would likely cause problems among those left behind. At the same time, he was a tough, longtime sailor who followed orders, traits that Shackleton admired.

McNeish was among the older members of the party, and the trip would be hard on him, but his carpentry skills would be essential in fixing the

Caird if she became damaged. He was also ingenious at making do with whatever was available. Moreover, McNeish was a bit of a wildcard. He had quit on Worsley when pulling a boat, and Shackleton didn't wish to burden Wild by leaving him on the island. Vincent's behavior was also unpredictable. Although he'd presented no problems since leaving Patience Camp, the boring and intensely stressful conditions of waiting could prompt poor behavior.

Amidst blizzard winds that reached 120 miles per hour, driving snow everywhere and launching anything unfastened, McNeish and Marston began to lay decking on the *Caird*. Sledge runners became ribbing, and plywood from boxes of stores provided the actual deck. A canvas cover provided a degree of waterproofing. The men put the *Docker's* mast inboard overlying the *Caird's* keel to add strength and hopefully prevent the boat from breaking apart in the heavy seas. The mast from the *Wills* became a mizzenmast on the *Caird*, giving her a third sail.

It was April 24. After 9 days, the weather and sea had calmed enough for the *Caird* to depart and for Worsley to get his first sightings. Knowing their position, he established that the single remaining chronometer of the initial 24 was accurate. This was good news. They could determine with precision their position during the boat trip—when and if the sun came out. A few days earlier, Shackleton had conferred privately with Macklin, one of the two surgeons, about how long the men might be able to survive. Perhaps a month, Macklin replied—not a reassuring assessment.

Wild and Shackleton had spent the night discussing how to maintain Elephant Island camp. If Shackleton hadn't returned by November, Wild should sail 140 miles to Deception Island, where whalers would arrive for the summer season. Shackleton wrote in his diary that Wild would be in charge of Elephant Island, in addition to other expedition details, in case he himself didn't survive. He concluded, "You can convey my love to my people and say I tried my best," and gave his diary to Wild.

Up since dawn making final preparations for their departure, the men feasted on a substantial send-off breakfast and joked with one another. They teased McCarthy about the dangers of getting his feet wet and cautioned Worsley about the consequences of gluttony. Crean, a womanizer, had to promise he'd spare a few ladies for those who were left behind on Elephant Island.

With difficulty, the explorers launched the *Caird*—an oar broke, the men labored hard to haul her through waist-deep surf, and once afloat, she almost capsized, dumping McNeish and Vincent into the sea. Vincent

4.1: Launching the *Caird* from Elephant Island for her voyage to South Georgia Island.

cursed and accepted dry clothes. McNeish just cursed. It took most of the morning for the *Wills* to shuttle supplies and ballast. Through the *Caird's* 2-by-4-foot cockpit, they loaded 6 weeks of food, two 18-gallon casks of fresh water and some 250 pounds of ice for drinking, 1,000 pounds of ballast rocks sewn into canvas bags along with another thousand pounds of loose rocks, two Primus stoves, six reindeer sleeping bags, two sextants, and navigational tables and charts sealed in a watertight box. The one functional chronometer hung around Worsley's neck.

Shortly after midday, the *Caird's* three sails went up amid cheers from the men in the *Wills* and on shore. The sails caught the wind as the sun shown brightly on the tiny craft headed due north. Orde-Lees wrote:

> They made surprising speed for such a small craft. We watched them until they were out of sight, which was not long, for such a tiny boat was soon lost to sight on the great heaving ocean; as she dipped into the trough of each wave, she disappeared completely, sail and all.

The *Caird* had taken the best of what was left of the material wealth of the Weddell Sea Party. The remnants of this once-invincible expedition could not have marooned on a more desolate island. The men's only meaningful chance for survival had slipped over the horizon to take on the Drake Passage. They were left without a seaworthy boat, chronometer, or sextant. They had little shelter, little in the way of stores, little more than rags for clothing, and three men with serious medical conditions: Blackborow, Rickinson, and Hudson, who had a large boil on his behind.

The men pulled the *Wills* onto the tiny beach, turned her over, and crowded underneath to take advantage of the best shelter available. The adrenalin surge prompted by the departure quickly dissipated. A betting man would have placed nothing of value on their making it out alive: first, the likelihood of the *Caird* reaching South Georgia was essentially zero. Second, no one knew to look for them on Elephant Island. In fact, no search at all had been mounted for the *Endurance* Party—World War I was in progress, and resources and attention were needed elsewhere. Third, the likelihood of having sufficient materials to mount another boat rescue attempt was vanishingly small. The men did, however, have absolute trust and confidence in the *Caird*'s team, showing optimism that help would come.

The men tried carving an ice cave in a nearby glacier, but their body heat melted the ice and made it too wet for habitation. Next, they constructed a shelter with piled-up rocks for sides and the two boats as the roof—a task that revealed just how enfeebled they were. Rocks that one man could normally lift effortlessly in one hand required two men to carry, and even that effort was exhausting. They used canvas, blankets, wood, and all manner of scraps to fill cracks in an attempt to keep out snow and wind, but to little avail.

The shelter was crowded. Some slept topside on the undersides of the overturned boats' seats and others on the ground, each choosing the best sleeping place he could find. The blubber stove that warmed their home was a constant source of irritating smoke and soot. At night, it was impossible to leave the shelter to urinate without stepping on someone or then tracking snow back in afterwards. In time the men stayed inside and urinated into a bucket. Whoever filled the bucket had to dump it outside. The men would listen carefully. If the bucket sounded nearly full, they would wait for another man to fill it. Hurley wrote, "Life here without a hut and equipment is almost beyond endurance."

Blizzard after blizzard tormented them. Macklin summed up their plight:

Everything deeply snowed over, footgear frozen so stiff that we could only put it on by degrees, not a dry or warm pair of gloves among us. I think I spent this morning the most unhappy hour of my life—all attempts seemed so hopeless, and fate seemed absolutely determined to thwart us. Men sat and cursed, not loudly but with an intenseness that showed their hatred of this island on which we had sought shelter.

During the second week of May, long before the *Caird* could have reached South Georgia, they began checking the ocean's ice condition and looking for a ship. There were no ships, of course, and on many days they were iced in and isolated from rescue. Life went on. They did what they needed to do. The doctors, Macklin and McIlroy, stayed busy. They pulled a bad tooth from one man and did what they could for infected hands, eyes, and the persistent saltwater boils and frostbitten feet. They monitored the boil on Hudson's behind, the gangrene in Blackborow's left foot, and kept an eye on Rickinson.

In mid June, McIlroy decided the time had come to amputate Blackborow's toes. Wild had the shelter converted into a makeshift operating room and cleared it of all the men except for the two invalids—Hudson, whose huge abscess kept him bedridden, and Greenstreet, whose frostbitten feet had not yet recovered. The men stoked the fire to raise the temperature to a stifling 80 degrees so the chloroform—the only anesthetic they had—would vaporize. Once Blackborow was unconscious, McIlroy removed his bandages, cut across his foot, exposed his gangrene toes, and cut them off, one by one. He then cleared away the remaining dead tissues and sewed up the incision.

It had been a tense hour. Shortly thereafter, Blackborow moaned, figured out where he was, and smiled at the two doctors, saying, "I'd like a cigarette." Taking a page from the *Encyclopedia Britannica*, McIlroy added some tobacco and rolled him one. Wild suggested that Macklin and McIlroy wash up with the pot of hot water that they had used to sterilize the instruments. They stripped to the waist, found a scrap of soap, and had their first bath in 9 months. The other men, meanwhile, retreated to the shelter of the wet ice cave to give each other haircuts.

Few other days had such purpose or anxiety. The days were usually gray and wet, if not miserable and boring. Greenstreet wrote, "Everyone spent the day rotting in their bags with blubber and tobacco smoke—so passes another goddam rotten day." Every once in awhile, however, the sun would emerge and revive spirits, awaken positive thoughts, and capture the transient beauty of the nearby glaciers and rugged mountains silhouetted against a crystal blue sky.

One day, and then 1 month, ran into the next. The men constantly discussed rescue, and each man regularly mounted a high place to look seaward. They didn't talk about what was on their minds. Orde-Lees wrote candidly in his diary:

> One cannot help but be a bit anxious about Sir Ernest. One wonders how he fared, where he is now and how it is that he has not yet been able to relieve us. The subject is practically taboo; everyone keeps their own counsel and thinks different, and no one knows just what anyone else thinks about it, and it is quite obvious that no one really dare say what they really do think.

The 2-year anniversary of their sailing from London, August 1, passed. For a month, Wild had predicted they'd be rescued "next week," but this optimism contrasted sharply with his standing request "that every scrap of cord and wool and all nails be carefully kept in view of the possibility of our having to make a boat journey to Deception Island." All obeyed and saved, but it was no secret that the two boats were wrecks and that the *Docker* had no sail or mast. The men did have five oars.

Despite the bleakness of their lives and prospects, Wild had masterfully held the spirits of Elephant Island's prisoners high for 3 months. His calm, steady leadership, combined with his absolute confidence in Shackleton's invincible capacity to deliver salvation, enabled all to believe "The Boss would be here tomorrow." Soon, that tomorrow would be today.

4.2: Wild's men passed their time on Elephant Island mostly waiting for a rescue ship to appear on the horizon.

§

On the afternoon of April 24, more than 3 months earlier, the *Caird* reached the bounding ice band and sailed east to find the channel Shackleton and Worsley had seen earlier in the day from their lookout on Elephant Island. Navigating through the broken, wind- and water-beaten ancient floes and bergs, their minds conjured all manner of images in nature's carvings of ice: castle, church, gondola, giraffe, swan, duck, crocodile head, bear, mosque, elephant, Swiss chalet, battleship, hyena, lion, penguin, and mushroom. Worsley wrote, "All the strange, fantastic shapes rose and fell in stately cadence, with a rustling, whispering sound and hollow echoes to the thudding seas, clear green at the water line, shading to a deep, dark blue far below, all snowy purity and cool blue shadows above."

In the late afternoon, they emerged into the open ocean and set sail. A strong wind pushed them due north into the east-flowing Drake Passage and away from the ice that had defined their reality for the past year and a half.

Shackleton and Worsley took the first watch that night while the others slept below. The southeast wind was cold, and every second wave broke over the stern quarter, drenching and chilling them both. They huddled together for warmth, a brilliant display of stars and the Southern Cross guiding them north.

Shackleton's element was snow and ice, not a small boat in the treacherous Drake Passage. Worsley believed they would succeed, but Shackleton was heavy with responsibility for those left behind. On the frozen land, a man had some slack—will and determination could make the difference between failure and success. Shackleton's physical strength, insight into human nature, self-confidence, and good judgment had served his team well. Here at sea, however, the forces of wind, water and ice give no quarter—one does not attain victory, only survival or death. Wanting the journey to end as quickly as possible, Shackleton asked Worsley if the strong southwest wind would persist long enough to carry them the 500 miles to Cape Horn.

"No," Worsley replied, "Not a chance."

"Do you know I know nothing about boat sailing?" Shackleton laughingly confessed.

"All right, Boss," Worsley replied, "I do."

After an uneventful night, dawn broke. The boat was 45 miles due north of Elephant Island. The wind shifted north and then west-southwest to create a wicked cross sea, with waves that washed over the deck from both sides. Water pounded into the open cockpit and leaked through the canvas cover, making it necessary to pump the boat every few hours. Pumping required two men, one to hold the icy brass cylinder in the bottom of the boat while the other operated the plunger. Within minutes, the holder's hands, even with mittens, would nearly freeze, and the men would have to exchange jobs.

Shackleton set the watch teams: he, Crean, and McNeish took the first 4-hour watch; Worsley, McCarty, and Vincent the other. Each man took a little more than an hour's stint at the helm. The other two, when not pumping, bailing, or working the sails, sat hunched below, smoking or talking in the "saloon," the space just forward of the cockpit where they stored food and cooked and served meals. Shelter from the weather was a relief, but the men could sit only while bent over, with knees, chest, and stomach bunched together, or concoct a half-lying, half-sitting position among boxes and gear, all the while soaked from water dripping or streaming in through the decking above.

Cooking and eating presented additional challenges. Because the *Caird* was always in motion and buffeted constantly by heavy seas, Crean and Worsley would put their backs against opposite sides of the boat and hold the Primus stove steady between their feet. Worsley would hold the pot on the stove, while Crean added whatever they were preparing. When Crean announced, "ready," six aluminum mugs appeared as a ring around the hoosh

4.3: Longitudinal section of the *Caird* showing cockpit, saloon just forward of the cockpit, ballast and stores on the bottom, and sleeping quarters in the bow.

pot, into which Crean scooped out equal servings. Each man then found a position in which he was able to place food in his mouth, but not so bent over that swallowing was impossible. It was a small cramped boat, but almost immediately they "talked of going for'ard or aft, of the watch coming on deck or going below, as though [they] were in a hundred-ton sailing craft."

Changing the watch was an ordeal. Sleeping quarters were a triangular area 5 feet at the base going 7 feet to a point in the bow and located on top of boxes with hard corners uncomfortable to move over or lie on. The height permitted only a hunched sitting position. From the saloon a man had to crawl through a narrow passage between thwart above and food boxes and ballast below. Sharp corners and edges as well as slippery hard rocks punished the crawler's knees and body. Then, as Worsley describes:

> Halfway through you paused for breath—you became exhausted
> and doubted if life was worth living, but then came a gentle nudge
> from the next man's head or shoulder against your after-end, and
> you again moved reluctantly forward. The crawl in [on] one side
> of the mast, out the other, of Weary Willies going below and Tired
> Tims coming "on deck" was such an operation that Sir Ernest took
> charge of the queue and directed order of march.

The southwest wind held for 2 days. At noon on the third day, when the sun made a rare, brief appearance, Worsley got his first sighting. Waiting for the sun to appear, Worsley knelt in the saloon with the sextant cradled under his chest to prevent it from being splashed. Shackleton sat next to him with pencil, logbook, and chronometer. At just the right moment, Worsley came on deck and knelt on the thwart, two men holding him fast. Exactly as the boat reached the crest of a wave and was momentarily steady, he sighted the sun in the sextant, snapped the altitude, and yelled, "Stop." Shackleton recorded the time while Worsley worked the numbers: 59° 46' south latitude, 52° 18' west longitude—128 miles north of Elephant Island. They had crossed from the "Screaming Sixties" into the "Raving Fifties" and were squarely in the Drake Passage.

Wind velocities of 150 to 200 miles per hour, normally found only in the most violent cyclones and hurricanes (typhoons), are common in the Drake Passage. Its huge waves, called Cape Horn Rollers, are a mile in length with heights of 50 to 100 feet. The "big ones" are 200 feet or more. They travel fast, 30 to 50 miles per hour. Charles Darwin wrote of these "Leviathans of the Deep" in 1833: "The sight … is enough to make a landsman dream for a week about death, peril and shipwreck." In rare moments of sunlight, the waves' cobalt blue is magical, but their appearance otherwise is a bleak, menacing gray reflecting the remorseless sky.

At noon on the fourth day the weather soured completely, with a fierce wind swinging around to the north. Showered by freezing rain and icy spray, the crew tacked against the wind to maintain a northerly direction, away from ice and perhaps into warmer temperatures. Every minute or two, the *Caird* rose to the crest of a huge wave, only to careen down the other side, repeatedly *ad nauseam,* until the terror of this roller-coaster ride became routine. The helmsman suffered the most—each hour's stint seemed like an eternity. After 12 hours of merciless pounding and pure misery just to stay in place, the wind shifted to the northwest, and the men were again able to maintain a northeast heading.

Day broke with the wind settling to a breeze, the best weather yet. Shackleton's sciatica began to act up. The men's legs and feet felt poorly. They were white and puffy from the constant cold and wet and had little or no movement. The wind shifted to the west that afternoon, driving the *Caird* to the northeast ever faster. The next day, a south-southwest gale pushed them even harder. An afternoon break in the sky allowed Worsley a second sighting—238 miles in 6 days.

The next day, the winds increased to 70 miles per hour, pushing the bow down. The waves washing over the stern tended to push the boat broadside to the seas, making steering difficult as she wallowed from side to side. The temperature dropped to 0°, indicating that the southwest wind was coming off pack ice, perhaps not far away. The *Caird* was taking on so much water that the men had to bail to augment the pump. Ice built up, forcing everyone to turn to and alternate between bailing and de-icing.

The men were making great headway, but not without taking a beating. As the afternoon waned, it was clear that they couldn't take any more. Coming about to face the storm, they dropped sail and put out the sea anchor. Attached to the bow, the sea anchor dragged as the wind pushed the boat to the northeast. With each cresting wave, the anchor slacked. The *Caird* slid sideways down the wave until the anchor rope again became taut and the boat yanked back, bow into the storm.

The furled sails soon iced-up and the *Caird* became top heavy. In pitching sea and gale force wind, Crean and McCarty ventured on deck to de-ice the sails before stuffing them into a hold already crammed full of gear, supplies, and men. Next, the oars lashed on the gunwales iced over, allowing water that came over the bow to channel into the cockpit and freeze on the decking. Shackleton, Worsley, Crean, and McCarthy crawled onto the ice-covered pitching deck to knock the ice off the oars. They tossed one set overboard, as no room remained below, and lashed the other set a foot and a half above the decking so water could flow freely under them and off the boat. After 30 minutes of nerve-wracking work, they crawled below, soaked to the skin and chilled to the core.

As the night wore on, the violent motion subsided. The *Caird* appeared to stabilize, and less water leaked into the saloon. At dawn, however, the reason became clear: the boat was completely encased in ice—a foot thick in places. The sea anchor rope had become an ice cable 8 inches thick, and the boat was riding 4 inches lower. Worsley was on watch and awoke Shackleton. After emerging from the cockpit and beholding the work of the night's weather, Boss roused the others. He then crawled onto the deck and began breaking off the ice with the blunt end of an ax. However, the waves didn't relent, and within 10 minutes he was too cold and stiff to safely continue. Shackleton gave the axe to Worsley. Each man took a 5-minute turn and passed on the ax. They had to take great care. If a man slipped overboard, there was no hope of rescuing him. The cold water would kill him in minutes.

In the hold, icicles were forming under the deck. The water in the bottom of the boat was not only turning to ice but also freezing up the pump. If the ice continued to accumulate below, the *Caird* would sink. Crean lit the Primus stove to warm the men and perhaps thaw things out. Topside, de-icing took the better part of 2 hours. Shackleton then called everyone below for hot milk and a rest near the stove. The men's body heat tipped the balance: the icicles melted, and the bilge pump thawed. Outside, however, the southwest gale raged on, and the ice buildup continued. They spent another unpleasant hour knocking it off. The men drank hot milk every 4 hours and kept the Primus burning for as long as they could tolerate the fumes, lighting it again once the air cleared. They endured another stressful night of waiting.

At dawn, the men cleared the ice. At mid-morning, they felt a momentary quiver. A large wave had lifted the *Caird* and a breaking wave had struck the boat. As she slid down the wave, the boat wallowed into the trough. The rope to the sea anchor had snapped from its persistent friction against the ice. Worsley and Shackleton knew instantly what had happened and shouted into the hole to get the jib. Crean and McCarthy cautiously crawled across the deck of the pitching, rolling boat. In what seemed like an eternity, they hoisted the small sail up the mainmast. The *Caird* came around into the wind. The helmsman now faced the wind and spray head-on while holding the boat into the storm.

By late morning, the wind had subsided slightly. Shackleton ordered sails hoisted. After 44 hours of pure hell just to stay afloat, the *Caird* came about to run with wind and current toward South Georgia. In the early afternoon an albatross appeared and for several hours floated above them on wings that never flapped. The bird was in its element, they were not. Yet the ever-positive McCarthy, with a happy grin across his face, greeted Worsley as he relieved him at the helm, "It's a grand day, sir." And so it was. As the day wore on, the storm moderated.

At noon the following day, the tenth one out, the sky cleared and the sun shone. Worsley's third sighting put them at 56° 13' south latitude, 45° 38' west longitude—433 miles from Elephant Island—more than halfway! The men were in the cockpit, stripped to their underwear and basking in the sun. Sleeping bags, boots, and clothing were all run-up to dry. Lansing writes of this scene:

> The sight that the *Caird* presented was one of the most incongruous imaginable. Here was a patched and battered 22-foot boat, daring to sail alone across the world's most tempestuous sea, her rigging festooned with a threadbare collection of clothing and half-rotten sleeping bags. Her crew consisted of six men whose faces were black with caked soot and half-hidden by matted beards, whose bodies were dead white from constant soaking in salt water.

The men were missing pieces of skin on their faces and fingers that marked frostbite damage. Their lower legs were marred from numerous trips across rocks and boxes of stores. Lansing continues:

> And all of them were afflicted with salt water boils on their wrists, ankles, and buttocks. But had someone unexpectedly come upon this bizarre scene, undoubtedly the most striking thing would have been the attitude of the men ... relaxed, even faintly jovial— almost as if they were on an outing of some sort.

The sun's energy works such wonders! Delivering 100 watts per square foot, the sun vaporizes water molecules quickly. The men were warmer and dryer than they had been in weeks and delighted in these rare conditions.

The good weather held through the following day. A southwest breeze gently pushed the boat. Waves washed rarely over the deck. All manner of clothing again adorned the rig. Worsley's calculations recorded a run of 52 miles the previous day, putting them within 250 miles of South Georgia. No longer totally miserable or focused only on staying afloat, the men began to imagine that reaching South Georgia was, after all, attainable.

Unfortunately, as the night wore on, the wind picked up. The sky filled with clouds, the sea rose, and the wind shifted to the south, causing waves to break over the starboard side. By morning, the men were as wet as ever, and the weather deteriorated through the day. By nighttime, gale force winds again made steering a challenge. To make matters worse, the main-mast pennant had become so shredded that it could no longer aid in setting course. The helmsman had only the feel of the boat and the line of breaking waves ahead to rely on.

Shackleton had just relieved Worsley and taken the helm at midnight when the sky astern appeared to lighten. Delighted, he shouted the good news to the others, only then to realize his mistake: this was the foam of a monstrous wave. He hunched down and yelled, "For God's sake, hold on! It's got us!"

Up, up, up they went, as the wave advanced. Tormented water engulfed and lifted the *Caird* almost into the air, jerking her violently forward and sideways in the same instant. Were they still upright? Thankfully, more quickly than it arrived, the foaming, tumultuous big one passed. Knee-deep in water, the men joyously realized that their foundering boat was upright. Grabbing whatever was at hand, they bailed madly—another wave would sink them for sure. Shackleton steered and watched intently astern, but nothing more emerged. After 2 hours of pumping and bailing, the men directed their attention to finding and stowing what had gone adrift. Crean located a soaked, clogged Primus stove and worked patiently for more than half an hour to revive it. In exasperation, he roundly cussed the stove—and it lit. All enjoyed mugs of hot milk.

Morning light revealed the Drake Passage in its normal temperament— 70 mile-per-hour-northwest winds pushing 100-foot rollers that were capable of finishing off what the previous night's wave had failed to do. Their course had to be northeast, but the northwest wind poured every wave onto the men in the cockpit and water into the hold. However, the desperateness of their plight and the puniness of their efforts against wind and water somehow passed unnoticed. According to Worsley's calculations,

4.4: The *Caird* and her crew were pushed to their limits in the Drake Passage.

South Georgia lay but 91 miles dead ahead. They had stood the test of the past 13 days.

The wind and seas rose to such ferocity that morning that they dropped sail and hove-to with the jib run-up the mainmast to come about into the wind. At dusk, as Crean began to prepare dinner, he discovered that their second cask of fresh water was salty and only half full. It must have been damaged when it fell off the *Wills* while being ferried out to the *Caird*. The men had no other water. The hoosh was salty and hard to swallow.

The boat had enough food for 2 weeks, but less than a week's worth of salty water. It was imperative that they land as soon as possible. Privately, Shackleton asked Worsley about his confidence in the calculations. He wasn't sure—he was perhaps within 10 miles—but he couldn't rule out mistakes. They had but one chance—3,000 miles of open ocean lay east of South Georgia.

The northwest gale eased off, and shortly after midnight they were sailing northeast once again. As day broke, the clouds opened up, but where were they? Worsley hadn't had a sighting since May 4, 3-days ago. He wrote: "Most unfavorable conditions for Obs. Misty with boat jumping

67

like a flea." The sun's image was blurry, but Worsley nevertheless took a batch of sightings, thinking that averaging them might increase accuracy. Position: 54° 38' south latitude, 39° 36' west longitude, 68 miles from South Georgia.

The crew had wanted to round the northwest end of South Georgia and sail down the northeast coast to the whaling stations, but they needed water and didn't know their precise location. Not wanting to overshoot the island, Shackleton set an easterly course to hit the west coast. No one lived there, nor were there any navigational aids.

As the day wore on, the men searched for biological signs of land: kelp, specific birds, and other land-indicating life. Night came, yet dawn brought nothing. If Worsley's calculations were correct, land was 10 miles away, but South Georgia's 10,000-foot peaks still weren't visible. At 10:30 a.m., Vincent spotted seaweed. Then a cormorant flew by—both were sure signs that land was within 15 miles. The mist partially cleared—still nothing in sight but rolling sea. Finally, a little past noon, McCarthy cried, "Land ho!" Out of the clouds, about 10 miles dead ahead, emerged a black cliff, blotched with snow. Shackleton spoke, "We've done it. We'll get a drink tonight. In a week we'll get them off Elephant Island." The men grinned in disbelief and relief.

An hour later they were close enough for Worsley to sketch the general contour of the land and compare it to his charts. This was most likely Cape Demidov, the northern headland of King Haakon Sound, 16 miles east of the western tip of South Georgia. Within 2 hours they were 3 miles off the coast. However, the sound of breakers and the sight of Cape Horn rollers smashing into rocks and cliffs cautioned them away. It was too dangerous to land here. Worsley's charts suggested two other landing places: King Haakon Bay, 10 miles east, and Wilson Harbor, 4 miles west. After another hour, the men were just 2 miles offshore but knew they couldn't reach either Wilson Harbor or King Haakon Bay before dark, so they headed seaward to stand off for the night.

After an unpleasant dinner prepared with the spoiled water, the weather worsened. Gale-force winds and cross seas that pushed one way then another hampered their retreat. At midnight they were some 18 miles off shore, only to be tormented by 40-foot rollers, snow, and freezing rain. They could barely see beyond the boat. How distant was the island? They had no idea. By noon the next day, the southwest wind was nearing 100 miles per hour. Ravaged by thirst, the men suffered with parched throats, swollen tongues, and cracked and bleeding lips.

Their situation was simultaneously good and bad. The wind was blowing the men onto South Georgia and away from their misery, but they couldn't see through the mist. When the clouds did finally part—revealing cliffs and glaciers that ran to the sea, with two steep mountains behind—they recognized their precarious position near the breakers. Worsley described it this way:

> The sky all torn, flying scud—the sea to wind'ard like surf on a shallow coast—one great roaring line of breaking seas behind another till lost in spume, spindrift, and the fierce squalls that were feeding the seas. Mist from their flying tops cut off by the wind filled with great hollows between the swells...
>
> It was the most awe-inspiring and dangerous position any of us had ever been in. It looked as though we were doomed—past the skill of man to save.

The crew had no choice but to set sail. Crean and Worsley crawled across the deck and hung on for dear life as they stood to lower the jib from the mainmast. As it dropped, the *Caird* dipped into a trough. The two men lurched forward to attach the jib to the forestay. McCarthy joined them on deck. On the heaving boat, it took all three men to raise the mainsail and mizzen.

Shackleton put the tiller over to bring the bow to the southeast. The southwest wind hit so hard that the *Caird* almost rolled over. Shackleton yelled for McNeish and Vincent to shift ballast to starboard to right the boat. Each wave smashed into the *Caird*, stopping its forward movement, but between waves she inched away from the breakers. The waves hit so forcefully that the bow planks opened slightly. Water poured in from the sides, deck, and cockpit. Three men pumped, one bailed, and one stood by to relieve whoever gave out.

Breaks in the sky revealed just how little progress the men were making. For 2 hours, they held their place relative to the breakers, but off the port bow loomed Annenkov Island, 5 miles off the coast of South Georgia. A series of reefs separated the tiny island from the coast. Although the bow was pointed southeast, the wind was driving the boat east-northeast, straight toward Annenkov! The men had to do the impossible—sail directly into oncoming seas and a gale-force wind. Their hope was to head southeast, hold close to the wind, and by some miracle sail past Annenkov.

While the others bailed, the helmsman watched the dark hulk of the little island grow ever closer and strained to discern any drift seaward. Each helmsman shouted to those bailing below that they were going to make it, but this was wishful thinking. The sound of the breakers drowned out the wind's incessant howling—the *Caird* was in the froth of backwash off Annenkov's cliffs. Worsley was at the helm and knew the end was near. Lansing wrote:

> Worsley thought to himself of the pity of it all. … [His diary of the entire journey] was now stowed in the forepeak of the *Caird*. When she went, it would go, too. Worsley thought not so much of dying, because that was now so plainly inevitable, but of the fact that no one would ever know how terribly close they had come.

He sat at the helm, awaiting the cracking sound of boat on rock, when the black of Annenkov yielded to the eastern sky. "She's clearing it! She's clearing it!" he yelled for all to hear.

The men stopped their frantic bailing and looked at stars and light to leeward. What had saved them? A mysterious offshore current? An eddy? By 9 p.m. they had passed Mislaid Rock, which stood less than a mile off Annenkov. The gale subsided and the wind shifted to south-southwest. The seas were still high, so they set a northwest course to avoid South Georgia. Everyone bailed water until midnight, after which the watch crew sufficed. Shackleton's group took the watch. Worsley's team went below to sleep.

The men had struggled—with every bit of life they had left—for 9 hours against a hurricane fiercer than any of them had ever witnessed. That same storm had sunk a 500-ton ship headed for South Georgia. All aboard were lost.

Early the next morning, as men maneuvered to change watch, Crean bumped against the thwart and knocked out the pin holding the mast clamp. The clamp opened, and the mast started to fall. On deck, McCarty saw it happening and caught the mast as it fell. The pin had likely been in an unstable position all that night. If it had come out during the hurricane, Worsley's musing just before they cleared Annenkov would have come true.

On May 10, shortly after daybreak, South Georgia appeared, about 10 miles distant. The crew headed directly for her, but the wind swung to the northwest and eased off, slowing their progress. At noon Cape Demidov was off the beam, and they headed east for King Haakon Bay. A strong headwind hindered their progress, however, so they dropped sails and rowed. Unfortunately, the tide began to flow south, conspiring with the wind to keep them offshore. Finally, by 3, the men spotted calm water in the bay

Side Note 7.
- Wind, water, ice, and immense waves beyond imagination tested the Caird's crew for 3 days when in sight of South Georgia. The men endured.
- How are we prepared for our unimaginable challenges? How can we prepare for our future tests?

and a channel through the reefs, but with just a few hours of daylight left, the distance was too far to row. Spending another night at sea was not an option, given their lack of water and the possibility of another storm, so under full sail, the *Caird* tacked into the wind and aimed for the channel. Four attempts failed. Night was falling, so they took the *Caird* a mile south, came about, and tried to run her into the wind one last time. This time she slipped through the breakers into the relative calm of King Haakon Bay. The crew dropped sail and rowed for a quarter hour, until Shackleton spotted a little cove beyond a small reef. Finding a narrow passageway, he guided her through. As the *Caird* scraped bottom, he jumped overboard, holding onto the remnant of the sea anchor rope. He held and steadied the boat as the other men followed. A small freshwater stream was but a few yards away. Instantly, the men fell to their knees and scooped up water. Then they stood and shook hands all around. The date was May 10, 1916—18 days since setting sail from Elephant Island.

CHAPTER 5

Crossing South Georgia

Finally ashore, Shackleton climbed some nearby rocks. Worsley tossed him a rope with which to secure the *Caird*. However, Shackleton, weak from so many days at sea, fell and dropped it. The strong turbulence in the cove swung the unsecured boat against the rocks and knocked the rudder free. The rudder drifted away into the night. The men were exhausted, their strength gone, but they had to beach the *Caird* safely out of the surf. They unloaded stores and gear and dumped the bags of ballast rocks overboard. The men were too feeble to haul the boat ashore. They first needed food and rest.

After tying the *Caird* to a rock, the weary crew sought shelter in a shallow cave near the beach. Shackleton took the first shift, watching for 3 hours instead of the usual one so the next watchman could have a bit more sleep. At 1 a.m. the *Caird* broke loose. Crean yelled for help. He managed to grab the bow rope, but was pulled in the water over his waist by the time help arrived. The men were able to beach the *Caird*, but they were still too weak to pull her out of the water. It took three men to hold her fast and all six to counter the undertow.

Shackleton's plan had been to stop for water, and then after a short rest, sail around the island to Leith Harbor, a distance of 130 miles. However, the situation had changed. With the rudder gone and the men badly in need of rest, the crew had to lighten the *Caird* so they could get her out of the breaking surf. McNeish and McCarthy removed the *Docker's* mast, decking, and other extra planking, thereby making her no longer sea worthy. Even then, it took the whole day to haul her ashore, a task that should have taken only an hour.

Shackleton was again in his element. He had but one choice if he were to rescue the men left on Elephant Island. His proposal? First, a few days of rest. Then a party of three—Shackleton, Worsley, and Crean—would attempt to hike across the island to the whaling stations, some 29 miles away. In 75 years of habitation, no one had ever crossed South Georgia. Could they do it? Ten-thousand-foot-peaks rose up in interior ranges, and a jumble of twisted mountains and glaciers bordered the sea on the eastern side. The interior was *terra incognita*—blank space on their map.

The next day, after a 12-hour sleep, Worsley and Shackleton set out to test the eastern shore of King Haakon Bay, hiking about 6 miles until stopped by a glacier. Access to the interior looked better at the end of the bay, so they decided they would sail there, and thus reduce their hiking distance to the whaling station by 6 miles. They'd hoped to sail in 2 days, but rain and wind changed their plans.

On the fourth day, early in the morning, the men pushed the *Caird* into the water. Bobbing in the surf was their errant rudder. The crew loaded the boat and replaced the steering oar with the repossessed rudder. The sun came out, and a gentle northwest wind caught the sails. Feeling lighthearted, the men began singing, as if on a picnic. They knew their luck was good. At noon, they arrived at a beach teeming with sea elephants—enough for food and fuel for years. With renewed strength they easily hauled the *Caird* out of the surf and turned her over. McCarthy built a stone foundation and stowed their sleeping bags inside. They had again seen the saddle in the coastal mountains through which Shackleton believed they could reach South Georgia's interior.

The next day was miserable. The men spent much of it under the boat. McNeish busied himself by making a small sled to haul gear for the trek. He put screws from the boat through the soles of three pairs of boots to allow for better traction on the packed snow and ice. The weather was hardly better the next day. Shackleton and Worsley hiked 3 hours to reach the saddle, but misty squalls obscured everything beyond it. Still, Shackleton remained convinced that this was the way to the interior.

Yet again, the men awoke to more bad weather. Shackleton was beside himself. Once more they reviewed their gear for the trek across the island. Shackleton insisted they travel extremely light: no sleeping bags, 3 day's food, a fueled-up Primus stove good for six meals, one pot, a half box of matches, two compasses, binoculars, 90 feet of rope made from knotted-together pieces, and a carpenter's adz for an ice ax. By evening, the sky began to clear.

Too anxious to sleep, Shackleton instead watched the sky. Worsley joined him at midnight. By 2 a.m., the remaining clouds gave way to a clear, moon-lit night. The men gathered for a hot meal. At 3 a.m., all but Vincent, who had severe rheumatism, walked the mile to the loaded sled. The three travelers bid farewell to McCarthy and McNeish and set a fast pace through the ankle-deep snow. In short order, they decided the sled wasn't worth the effort, and each took his share of the load. At the head of the bay, they climbed 2,500 feet up the steep, snow-covered rise to the saddle, where they then headed east. At 5 a.m., unable to see more than a few yards ahead, they roped themselves together. Dawn increased their visibility through the fog, revealing a large, snow-covered lake to their left. This was great luck—travel would be easy on a flat lake—so for an hour, they hiked toward it. Strangely, they encountered crevasses—they knew that glaciers do not end in lakes. As sunrise came, the fog dissipated completely. The "lake" ran to the horizon. Unfortunately, they had been walking toward the northern coast on a glacier that ended in Possession Bay. They couldn't walk from there along the shore to the whaling stations.

The error had cost them precious time. If caught at night by a blizzard or at a high altitude, they would be dead. Returning to their original position, they headed east. The day was spectacularly beautiful—the scenery beyond sublime. The men were traveling an unmapped area, rising steeply toward a ridge of five exposed, bare-rock, finger-like projections with saddles or passes between them. The only sounds were those of boots and legs against the snow and the swishing of the rope that tied them together. The men would walk for 15 minutes, and then rest for a minute by flopping on the snow and breathing deeply. Their route due east led toward the lowest of the four passes and between two peaks on the right side of the ridge. After a 30-minute breakfast break, they headed for the pass. Reaching it a little after 11, they peered down a sheer drop into a chasm some 1,500 feet below. To the left were ice cliffs and crevasses. To the right were glaciers that dropped down to the sea. Dead ahead, and far below them, was their destination: an upward-sloping snow field about 8 miles in length.

They walked downward for an hour, around the second peak, and then up toward the pass. After lunch, they began the steep ascent. Halfway up, they had to cut steps in the snow ice. The men pushed themselves hard—climb, rest, climb, rest. By mid-afternoon they'd reached the second pass, only to look down on a descent that was even more difficult than the first.

The men retreated again, but stayed higher on the third peak. Positioned at 4,500 feet, they could see fog rolling into the valley behind and below. They needed to reach the next valley before nightfall. Switch-backing down and across the steep slope, often cutting steps, they soon reached an ice ridge between the peaks that formed the third gap. The descent was

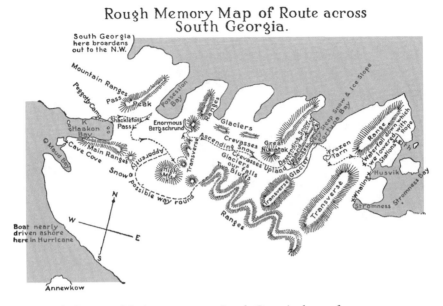

5.1: Worsley's map of their route across South Georgia drawn from memory.

less treacherous, but Shackleton avoided the route out of concern for safety. Zigzagging downward, they hiked toward the northernmost gap, but soon encountered a huge, chasm, some 200 feet deep and 2,000 feet long—perhaps created by frequent gales. With purpose they trekked around the abyss. As darkness fell, they finished cutting steps in the steep slope that led up to the razorback of ice that formed the crest of the fourth gap.

Shackleton called to the others as he straddled the ice ridge. They peered down a sheer descent into the distant valley that was quickly fading in the gathering fog and diminishing light. Far below, the steep slope appeared to level off. It was getting cold. Fog that had filled the valley behind them was now drifting between them and into their view downwards. Shackleton said, "We'll try it." He swung over the edge and began cutting steps in the ice-hard snow. One step at a time they descended. After half an hour they had moved only 200 yards. The surface of the snow ice had softened, indicating a decrease in slope, but the slope was still too steep for walking. Shackleton realized that the excruciatingly slow decent was futile—the temperature was well below freezing and the men exposed on an ice cliff 4,000 feet up. He cut a shelf. The men huddled together in the darkness. Boss came to the point—freeze to death here in a few hours or get lower fast.

With a boyish grin, he suggested they slide. Crean and Worsley were shocked. What was Boss thinking? What was below them? A steep drop-off?

5.2: Worsley, Crean and Shackleton hike around chasm on trek across South Georgia.

A wind-carved chasm? Rocks? Impatiently Shackleton asked "Can we stay here?" The others reluctantly concurred. Unroping themselves, each coiled a portion of the rope on the ice and sat on it. Like kids on a toboggan—Worsley's legs wrapped around Shackleton's waist and his arms on his shoulders, with Crean similarly positioned on Worsley—they shoved off into the darkness. Lansing described the slide:

> They seemed to hang poised for a split second, then suddenly the wind was shrieking in their ears, and a white blur of snow tore past. Down … down … They screamed—not in terror necessarily, but simply because they couldn't help it. It was squeezed out of them by the rapidly mounting pressure in their ears and against their chests. Faster and faster—down … down … down!

Within several minutes they had descended 3,000 feet, and then, after leveling off, collided gently with a snow bank. Laughing uncontrollably, and with hearts pounding, the men stood with new rips in their trousers watching the fog descend from the gap in the mountains far above.

Fearing their slide might trigger an avalanche, the men moved away quickly before digging a hole in the snow for the Primus and fixing dinner. When the common pot of hoosh was ready, each took a turn eating to ensure equitable distribution. Shackleton accused Crean of having the biggest spoon, Crean replied: "Holy smoke, look at the Skipper's mouth!" In the darkness of the night, Worsley used their distraction to sneak another spoonful.

Shackleton had contemplated making a snow cave and resting for the night, but decided to push on instead. They roped up and trekked on in the darkness, picking their way up the slope carefully and watching for crevasses. About an hour later, a full moon rose over the mountains, making travel easier and raising their spirits. A little after midnight, they were at 4,000 feet on a ridge that sloped off to the northeast toward what they anticipated would be Stromness Bay. They headed down. After about another hour, they saw water and an off-shore island. Concluding that it must be Mutton Island in Stromness Bay, they continued on enthusiastically, identifying expected landmarks as they went, their tired bodies invigorated by knowing that civilization was but a few hours away.

Crean saw a crevasse. Looking ahead, more crevasses appeared. The men were descending on a glacier. But wait—no glaciers flowed in Stromness Bay! They had been tricked by seeing the pattern they wanted to see.

Worsley determined from his charts that it was likely Fortuna Bay—Stromness Bay laid farther east. They about-faced and marched back up once again, Shackleton in the lead. The men stayed roped together for almost the entire trip because of the threat posed by crevasses and steep slopes. Knowing just how exhausting it was to break trail, Crean and Worsley offered more than once to take the lead, but Shackleton cheerfully refused. Shortly before dawn, after several exhausting hours of climbing, they had regained altitude and rounded Fortuna Bay.

Ahead was a line of ridges with a small pass. The men were spent. Huddled behind a rock for shelter from the wind and blowing snow, they sat on their walking sticks and wrapped their arms around each other for warmth. Worsley and Crean immediately fell asleep. Shackleton, too, caught himself nodding off, but knowing that sleep could slip into death at times like this, he resisted for 10 minutes. He then woke the others and told them they had slept for half an hour. Refreshed, but stiff-kneed, they awkwardly headed toward the gap 1,000 feet above them. An hour later, they peered down a gentle slope to see the hills around Sromness Bay in the distance. No mistake this time—Shackleton had identified the unique Z-shaped stratification on a rock formation across the bay.

With a new sense of success in their strides, the men headed down and then stopped for breakfast. While Crean and Worsley cooked their last hot meal, Shackleton cut ice steps up a nearby ridge to look ahead. In the distance he saw what appeared to be a precipice. As he climbed down, he heard a faint sound: perhaps it was the 6:30 a.m. steam whistle that awakened workers at the whaling station. Worsley, upon hearing the news, checked his chronometer: 6:50 a.m.. Exactly at 7:00, they heard the steam whistle calling the men to work. Shaking hands all round, Shackleton commented, "Never did music sound so sweet to [my] ears as that whistle." Worsley belted out, "Yoicks! Tallyho!" It was the first sound of civilization they'd heard in 18 months.

Shackleton chose the most direct route toward the precipice he had seen earlier. They walked a half mile down and across a slope that suddenly became treacherously steep. Keeping the rope taut, Crean and Worsley lowered Shackleton as he cut ice steps for 50 feet, then carved out an ice shelf. They joined him on the shelf. The men repeated the process several more times before noticing that the ice chips that Boss was cutting below were bouncing off the slope into space. They were approaching a vertical cliff! Worsley recommended that they retrace their route to find a safer one. Disregarding caution, Shackleton said, "No, we'll try it." For 100 yards, Shackleton cut steps horizontally across the cliff until they were able to continue their vertical descent. It took the men close to 3 hours to descend 1,000 feet.

Exhausted to the core, they pushed on across a glacier that descended into Fortuna Bay, then up toward Stromness Bay with its three whaling stations, each in its own cove. Husvik was to their north, Leith dead ahead, and Stromness to the south. Boss decided that Stromness was the most accessible. They angled to the right, up into rough country. Shortly after midday, standing on a 2,500-foot summit, they gazed down upon the Stromness Bay station with a mixture of amazement, relief, and exhaustion. Shaking hands, they silently watched two whalers plying their way across the bay and tiny figures moving along the wharfs and among the buildings. After a long silence, Shackleton quietly said, "Let's go down."

Below them, a steep, ice-covered, bowl-shaped slope descended toward the station. To their left, across the bowl's rim, a small, stream-cut valley also led toward the station. Worsley wanted to take the direct route down the slope, but Shackleton, his safety-first temperament revived, thought it too risky, so they headed toward the valley. After an hour, the sides of the valley steepened, ending at a small stream. By mid-afternoon the men, walking in knee-deep ice-cold water, headed toward a 25-foot waterfall. The valley's walls were too steep to climb. They had a choice: walk a mile around the falls, or rope down the falls. They looked at the falls, then each other. No one liked the choices. Having nothing to which to tie the rope, Worsley dropped one end over the waterfall until it touched the bottom. He then ran his end over a boulder and kicked the remaining 6 feet underneath the rock, hoping it would not be pulled out by his weight. Shackleton and Worsley lowered down Crean, the heaviest man. Worsley then held the rope while Shackleton descended. Worsley, the lightest and most nimble, slid down while the other two waited below to catch him should the rope pull free. It didn't!

Finally, they were but a mile from the station. Approaching civilization, they became self-conscious of their appearance. Worsley took four rusty safety pins that he had hoarded for almost 2 years and mended the worst rips in his pants. It didn't help much. The men had just trekked 40 miles in 36 hours without rest and were, as Worsley wrote, "[r]agged, filthy, and evil-smelling; hair and beards long and matted with soot and blubber; unwashed for three months, and no bath nor change of clothing for seven months."

The first people they saw were two boys. Both promptly bolted in fright. Next was an old man. He fled too. Reaching the wharf, Shackleton asked the foreman to take them to Mr. Sørlle, the station manager. He led the men to the manager's house and left them outside.

Inside, the foreman told Sørlle, "There are three funny-looking men outside, who say they have come over the island and they know you. I have left them outside." Sørlle opened the door. Seeing them, he stepped back in shock. After a long pause, he said, "Well, who the hell are you?"

Stepping forward, Shackleton said, "Don't you know me?"

"I know your voice. You're the mate of the *Daisy*."

"My name is Shackleton."

That night, Sørlle directed a whaler to take Worsley to King Haakon Bay. The next day they picked up McCarthy, McNeish, and Vincent, but the weather was so bad that they couldn't return to Stromness until the following day. For the crossing of South Georgia luck had been on their side, however. Norwegians at the whaling stations noted that on no other day and night that winter, other than those when they crossed, would the weather have allowed a man to survive in South Georgia's interior.

Less than 3 days after they had walked into Stromness, Shackleton, Worsley, and Crean were aboard the whaling ship *Southern Sky*, headed for

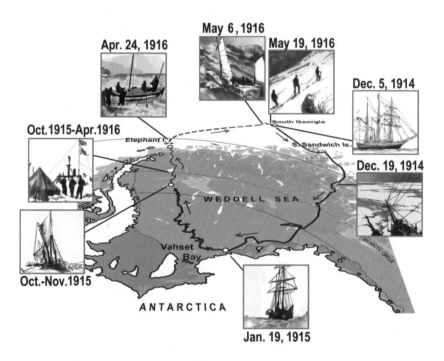

5.3: Pictorial summary and map of the *Endurance* Party's path.

Elephant Island. The other three men would soon sail for England. The *Southern Sky* was so laden with coal for the 1,600-mile trip to and from Elephant Island that water was close to washing over the deck. A hundred miles from Elephant Island, the weather turned cold. As they closed on the island, sea ice became thick and dense. At 60 miles, the steel-hulled whaler could penetrate no further. Much disappointed, Shackleton aborted the rescue attempt and steamed for the Falkland Islands.

After 3 days of poor weather and heavy seas, the *Southern Sky* reached Port Stanley. Shackleton requested a ship from the British Navy, but the Admiralty could provide nothing until October, a wait Shackleton considered too long for the men still stranded on Elephant Island. After 10 days of seeking a ship, the Uruguayan government offered the trawler *Instituto de Pesca No. I*. Shackleton accepted. The ship steamed from Montevideo, arriving at Port Stanley on June 10. Shackleton and his crew headed south.

Three days later, still 20 miles offshore, they encountered the same thick pack ice. For hours they steamed along its outer edge, looking for a way through. Finding a promising area of loose ice, Worsley entered the pack, only to be stopped by stressed engines. They backed out at once. A beset steel vessel would be doomed. The coal supply was down to 3 days, leaving retreat the only option. The engine knocked badly as they labored through a gale to reach Port Stanley just before the coal supply was exhausted. The crew wanted to make another attempt, but the trawler was slow and required too much coal for success, except under perfect conditions, which they hadn't had.

Shackleton, Worsley, and Crean then booked a steamer to Punta Arenas, Chile, in the Straits of Magellan, hoping to find a vessel capable of rescuing their comrades. The local British community raised 1,500 pounds to charter *Emma*, a 40-year-old oak-hulled schooner. It departed on July 12, and was towed for 50 miles by the Chilean steamer, *Yelcho*. Despite foul weather, they reached the pack some 100 miles from Elephant Island. Several more days passed as they sought a way south to the island, a task that involved entering the pack several times. The schooner's engine failed, but for several days under sail they continued to seek a passage south without success. Then the sails iced up, forcing a third retreat. Encountering a major storm, it took the men almost 2 weeks to sail to Port Stanley. They arrived August 8, almost a month after they had departed Punta Arenas.

A cable awaited Shackleton from the Admiralty informing him that the *Discovery* from England would be arriving in about 6 weeks. For Shackleton, it might as well have been 6 years. He wanted to be south just on the outside chance that the ice would clear long enough for them to slip in and get the men out. They returned to Punta Arenas. Immediately, Shackleton asked the Chilean government to lend him the *Yelcho*, the only suitable vessel in the region. They agreed. On August 25, the next day, they departed.

The weather was perfect. Five days later, on August 30, they neared Elephant Island, encountering fog but no pack ice. Worsley piloted the *Yelcho* as close to the camp as possible while Shackleton strained through his binoculars. "There are only two, Skipper!" A few moments later, "No, four!" Then, "I see six—eight—ten…" Until Shackleton cried with joy, "They are all there! Every one of them! They are all saved!"

PART 2

WHY DID THE
ENDURANCE PARTY
SURVIVE?

Shackleton and his 27 men should have disappeared into the vast Weddell Sea, never to be seen again and be no more than a footnote in the history of Antarctic exploration. But all 28 men survived. Individuals familiar with the *Endurance* story have offered reasons why.

CHAPTER 6

Message from the *Endurance* Party's Survival

People familiar with the *Endurance* Party's story are impressed with its unlikely outcome. Why did the men survive? Scholars and lay people alike have offered reasons.

Discipline, Leadership, Optimism, Skills, Talents, and Teamwork

Topping nearly everyone's list is Shackleton's unsurpassed leadership. He had an exceptional capacity to assess a man's character, an ability to elicit an almost unwavering confidence in his leadership, and a deep understanding of how to survive in the Antarctic. Could the *Endurance* Party have persevered without him? Few individuals, if any, think so.

Shackleton owed his spectacular achievement to several conditions associated with successful expeditions of discovery. Almost every man met Shackleton's standards for character, personality, and capacity to fit in, and all possessed a unique ability or professional skill that was needed for the expedition. Many of his team had served with him before, so they knew each other and had proven their worth and compatibility. Wild, the second in command, fit in especially well. As one of three men who accompanied Shackleton on his failed 1909 attempt to reach the South Pole, Wild displayed a calm, easy-going personality, under laid by an invincible inner toughness, all of which blended well with Shackleton's overt, confident, engaging, and sometimes volatile character.

A new member of the team was hired if he measured up during his initial terse interview with Boss. Worsley, a walk-in who Shackleton hired after the briefest of encounters, proved to be among the best of the choices, if not the very best. It is hard to imagine a successful boat trip to Elephant Island, no less the incredible 800-mile voyage to South Georgia, without his guidance.

Most of the men had served in the navy or merchant marine and participated in expeditions. Disciplined, accepting of rules, and accustomed to living in close quarters, they knew life at sea and were hardened by it. They had, for the most part, positive, can-do attitudes and were good team players. Testament to the high quality of the Weddell Sea Party members was the fact that none of their diaries mentioned physical violence. Only once did someone refuse an order. Shackleton never forgave McNeish. Anarchy was absolutely unacceptable.

After the *Endurance* was crushed, the party's goal of crossing the Antarctic continent turned to one of survival. When walking to land failed, the men were forced to accept that events beyond their influence would dictate their fate. Only by assessing each situation as it arose—and acting in a timely manner—did the men eventually get home. If an approach failed, Shackleton's team planned again. The men were ingenious at pooling their diverse talents and using limited resources to craft what they needed: a blubber-fired cook stove, a boat capable of sailing in the Drake Passage, boots with screws for cleats to traverse South Georgia's interior of ice-clad mountain passes.

Good Luck

Under Shackleton's leadership, the men never gave up. They bonded together to face the stark reality of their isolation. Nevertheless, chance events and fortuitous decisions were also incontrovertible elements of their survival.

We can identify numerous incidents in which a different decision would have likely spelled catastrophe. When a storm blew Ocean Camp to within 5 miles of Patience Camp, Shackleton—on Worsley's insistence—sent a group of men to Ocean Camp to retrieve the *Stancomb Wills*. Worsley wrote, "If it comes to boats, we shall be far safer in three; with only two it would be a practical impossibility to bring 28 men alive through a boat voyage of any length."

Shackleton ordered two marches in the fall and winter of 1915. Trekking to land was the primary plan. It appeared to be the best, if not the only, secure way to escape the sea and be rescued. Fortunately, Shackleton eventually abandoned trekking for the safety of the group and because he accepted the physical impossibility of a successful outcome—the warm spring weather had created random patches of open water and transformed the ice's surface to mush. Trekking could have continued with disastrous consequences.

On April 9, 1916, they had taken to the boats because their floe was disintegrating before their eyes. That night they made camp on another floe. All but Shackleton were asleep when the floe cracked under his feet and under a tent. Shackleton was able to pull Holness from the water just as the pieces slammed back together. Then the floe cracked open again, very quickly, leaving the *Caird* and one group of men separated from the rest of the party. Events led to Shackleton drifting away into the mist on a piece of ice. The men launched a boat and rescued him. It is hard to imagine that a replay of this day would have ended the same way, and many alternative outcomes could have led to their demise.

The next night the men badly needed sleep, so Shackleton decided to make camp on a floe-berg. While pulling the boats onto the ice, Stevenson fell into the frigid water. Hurley, Shackleton, and Wild almost fell too. Wave action had under-cut the exposed ice of the floe-berg, leaving somewhat rotten overhangs of ice. McNeish, who was alone near the edge when the ice overhang he was standing on broke off, jumped in the nick of time back onto solid ice. The next morning, pack ice surrounded the floe-berg to the horizon. The men waited anxiously most of the day while ice-laden waves crashing into all sides chewed up the floe-berg. Then suddenly a mysterious current cleared the ice south of the floe-berg. Shackleton commanded, "Launch the boats. Chuck in the stores any old way." It was bad luck to have camped on the floe-berg in the first place, and that decision led to opportunities for things to go poorly, but good fortune was with them.

Their lucky streak continued. They had escaped from the disintegrating ice into the Bransfield Strait in lifeboats never designed for such a place. In fact, no open boat had much prospect of completing a 6-day voyage even under ideal conditions. That they managed to endure the last 3 days of their boat trip is hard to accept. Even more incredible was the resilience of the *Docker's* crew the last night and at dawn when Worsley had to be kicked into consciousness just in time to bring the boat around to escape offshore waves from sinking them. Additionally, what was the probability that the separated boats would both round the north end of Elephant Island and end up at the same landing place on the northwest side later in the morning?

When the men arrived on Elephant Island, only one of the initial 24 chronometers was operational—another fortuitous outcome. Without knowing the exact time, Worsley could not use a sextant and navigational tables to establish their position. They would have had to use dead reckoning to reach South Georgia, an unbelievable challenge would have been even more difficult without a chronometer.

Sailing some 800 miles in a 22½-foot, open-cockpit boat from Elephant Island to South Georgia through the Drake Passage is in a league by itself. Living through 200-foot-high rollers, 100-mile-per-hour winds, de-icing the boat and setting sails under horrendous conditions, staying afloat in a hurricane, enduring the last days without good water, and navigating to hit a 25-mile wide target with only four sun sightings for navigation was nothing short of a miracle.

Shackleton describes a most notable stroke of good fortune after surviving the hurricane that sank a 500-ton ship and clearing Annewkow Island aboard the *Caird*:

> … through a rift in the flying mists, we got a glimpse of the huge crags of the island and realized that our position had become desperate. … I think most of us had a feeling that the end was very near. … [J]ust when things looked their worst, they changed for the best. … Almost as soon as the gale eased, the pin that locked the mast to the thwart fell out. It must have been on the point of doing this throughout the hurricane, and if it had gone nothing could have saved us.

After landing on the uninhabited side of South Georgia Island, Shackleton, Worsley, and Crean, in a 36-hour forced march, crossed for the first time the island's unmapped interior during the only calm period that winter. This successful crossing by itself had an infinitesimally small probability.

Supernatural Forces

The *Endurance* Party was superstitious. Worsley admitted that it was a dream that motivated him to walk down Burlington Street and thereby coming upon Shackleton's office. On ship once, when the wind was blowing favorably out of the southwest, Lansing recounted, "That night Shackleton wrote, almost timorously, 'This may be the turn in our fortune.' By now the wind was not taken lightly. 'It is spoken of with reverence,' Hurley observed, 'and wood must be touched when commenting thereon.'"

Although formal religious services or acts were not part of their routine, nor did I find anything about prayer in the books written by Shackleton and Worsley on the *Endurance* story, the men did believe in God. (Note: 100 years ago "Providence" and "higher Power" meant God.)

Shackleton, upon hearing distant noises from the grinding and jostling of million-ton ice floes, thought, "The ice moves majestically, irresistibly. Human effort is not futile, but man fights against the giant forces of Nature in a spirit of humility. One has a sense of dependence on the higher Power." Worsley noted:

> I learnt afterwards that we had crossed the island during the only
> interval of fine weather that occurred that winter. There was no
> doubt that Providence had been with us. There was indeed one
> curious thing about our crossing of South Georgia, a thing that
> has given me much food for thought, and which I have never been
> able to explain. Whenever I reviewed the incidents of that march I
> had the sub-conscious feeling that there were four of us, instead of
> three. Moreover, this impression was shared by both Shackleton
> and Crean.

Despite these beliefs, the men did not expect to avoid death by dreaming something or touching wood, nor did they count on some supernatural force saving them.

Verifiable Evidence-Based Knowledge Acquired by the Scientific Method

Clearly, the odds of survival were vanishingly small, despite the team's undefeatable optimism and skills, Shackleton's superb leadership, incredible good luck, and belief in the supernatural. Yet the men did survive! Was there a fundamental systemic factor missed by those who have written on why they beat the odds?

Two days after ordering the *Endurance* abandoned, Shackleton called the men together, instructing them to take only 2 pounds of personal gear. Lansing describes Boss's actions:

> [Shackleton] reached under his parka and took out a gold ciga-
> rette case and several gold sovereigns and threw them into the
> snow at his feet. Then he opened the Bible Queen Alexandra had

given them and ripped out the [inscribed] flyleaf and the page containing the Twenty-third Psalm. He also tore out [a] page from the Book of Job. Then he laid the Bible in the snow and walked away.

Here is a fundamental explanation, a grounding principle, of why the *Endurance* Party survived. We must acknowledge human-created conventions of economics, but the relevant perspective is not a fabricated valuing system but rather the rules of physics and biology. We must respect spiritual and religious beliefs as a fundamental part of human nature; however, the principles of the natural sciences are most pertinent when making important decisions. It is verifiable evidence-based reality that ultimately dictates the outcome of human actions. Shackleton clearly expressed this conviction during a private conversation with Wild and Worsley in early July 1915, when he told Worsley, "What the ice gets, the ice keeps"—the ship will likely be crushed.

When trekking across snow and ice, the weight one carries determines the required energy. The available energy depends upon animal physiology and accessible food. Shackleton accepted these rules of physics and biology when he limited personal items to 2 pounds soon after abandoning the ship. He reinforced his adherence to these rules a week later when the men returned to the ship for scavenging and found Hurley's photographic negatives. Shackleton had 400 of 550 glass negatives smashed, thereby removing any temptation to save more.

After failing twice to trek with minimal weight, Shackleton accepted the rules of the natural sciences that dictated it was not physically possible for them to walk to land. Economic valuing and religious beliefs cannot change the rules of physics and biology. Without question, Shackleton and the men of the *Endurance* Party did universally accept evidence-based reality as illuminated through the natural sciences and their rules—what we call today biological and physical reality, or biophysical reality. Shackleton and his men knew and accepted that the rules of these disciplines were their masters. They acted accordingly throughout the expedition.

The explorers embraced the rules of biology expressed in medicine when deciding what they would take or leave behind. Lansing writes, "For some men, the two-pound limit on personal gear was relaxed for special reasons. The two surgeons, of course, were permitted a small amount of medical supplies and instruments." An acceptance of biological rules was affirmed in what Worsley wrote about Shackleton, who needled him about his appetite for seal meat:

Nevertheless, he encouraged our hunting, for he recognized that not only did we need large quantities to feed the men and dogs, but that it was vital for keeping off scurvy [because fresh meat provides sufficient vitamin C to prevent the disease]. Scurvy has always been the foe of Polar explorers, and Shackleton, owing to his scientific methods and common sense, was practically the first to make long journeys without any of his men falling victims to it—which, to my mind, is an even greater achievement than his important geographical discoveries.

What follows are more examples illustrative of the men's adherence to the rules of verifiable, evidence-based science.

Worsley was fascinated by the mock suns but knew they were optical illusions. Equally so were the mirages of ice bergs boiling into the sky and the "barrier cliffs thrown up in the air, where we know all is deep sea." These men understood the value of science in explaining that what one saw wasn't always as it appeared.

The dogs—whose primary function was to pull the sleds to harvest killed seals and sea lions and later to retrieve stores from the *Endurance* and abandoned campsites—proved also to be good companions to the men. Nevertheless, in January and March 1916, Shackleton ordered them killed. As important as the dogs' companionship and usefulness had been, their fate came down to energy. Food was a limited resource—what the dogs ate was not available to the men.

Soon after the *Endurance* was crushed and the men began living on the ice, Shackleton told Green to put seal blubber in their hoosh. At first, almost everyone picked out the fatty globs and tossed them away, but that changed. As Worsley described, "We are ready to eat anything, especially cooked blubber, which none of us would tackle before. Probably living totally in the open and having to rely on food instead of fire for body heat makes us think so much of food." The rules of physics and biology had changed their minds. The men could have refused the blubber—the Norse (Europeans), who successfully established the Western Settlement on Greenland during a warm period beginning around 1,000 Common Era (CE)—died from starvation when the little ice age came beginning in 1,300 CE. Native Thule people living in the same area thrived on fish and ringed seals. Archeological evidence indicates that the Norse, who shunned heathen ways, elected not to eat either kind of animal.

Worsley wrote:

[I]f we did not exercise before turning in we were cold all night, so that we could get hardly any sleep. If on the other hand we took enough exercise to warm us, the ravenous hunger engendered had almost the same effect. We had to learn how to control our exercise so that it would be just sufficient to prevent us from feeling frozen without producing sufficient appetite to keep us awake. Eventually we managed to reduce this to a science, achieving a nicely balanced adjustment between hunger and cold.

On March 31, 1916, when still on the floes, Worsley got his first sighting in 6 days. They were 28 miles further north from their last fixed position, yet they experienced strong winds out of the north most of the time. Although the winds should have pushed them southward, they had been drifting north under the influence of a strong northerly current. Again, on the boat journey to Elephant Island, Worsley was off by 50 miles that led Shackleton to change once again their destination. Our senses often deceive. Scientifically developed instruments extend our capacity to know reality, as they did for the *Endurance* Party.

Shackleton chose not to launch the boats from the floe until absolutely necessary. By April 9, 1916, the Patience Camp floe had been reduced from more than 3 million square yards to a triangle of about 900 square yards, and it was continuing to break up. Only then, when the wind dropped and the floes dispersed, did Shackleton calmly order, "Launch the boats."

Rowing and sailing such small boats in the Bransfield Straight and the Drake Passage required careful attention to the principles of mass, fluid dynamics, aerodynamics, force, and gravity. The boats had to be packed, including ballast if necessary, to keep the center of gravity as low as possible while maintaining adequate free board to prevent swamping. Dead reckoning and sailing required the men to integrate knowledge of wind and water forces as well as the boat's physical characteristics.

The *Endurance* Party survived because of cooperation, discipline, luck, superb leadership, and an unflinching belief in verifiable, evidence-based reality. The leaders understood and used what the evidence-based sciences and other similarly grounded disciplines had elucidated about how the natural world works. The entire party, especially its leaders, accepted this knowledge as the brass tacks from which to make important decisions.

PART 3
NATURE'S RULES AND DECISION MAKING

Modern society faces several major, interdependent difficulties—not unlike those that Shackleton's men experienced—but on a global scale. Survival for the Weddle Sea Party 100 years ago was as challenging then as the continuance of modern civilization is now. Here lies the ultimate value of the *Endurance* Party story: it is a parable for our times that embodies a pattern of beliefs and actions that we might emulate to enable our descendants to enjoy a prosperous and long lived future.

CHAPTER 7

Nature's Rules

Looking back on the *Endurance* story, we can surmise that if Shackleton had adhered tightly to the science he knew, this story of survival—albeit interesting—would probably not have been as notable. The *Endurance* was likely the strongest ship ever built in Norway at the time aside from the *Fram*, the ship that delivered Amundsen to Antarctica when he beat Scott to the South Pole. There was, however, a critical difference between the two ships. The *Fram* was built with a completely round bottom so that pressure from solid Antarctic ice would push her up preventing the ship from being crushed. In contrast, the *Endurance*, which was built for polar bear hunting in the Arctic, had straight walls above a rounded bottom portion that might allow Antarctic ice under pressure to hold and crush her. Shackleton knew this basic physics; however, the situation dictated purchase of the *Endurance*. She was available and offered at a discounted price.

Are we making similar short-sighted, economically based decisions today? Are we failing to employ systemically the rules of the natural sciences and evidence-based disciplines to resolve the world's environmental challenges? The story of the *Endurance* Party has made clear what too few people accept: the more consistent our actions are with the rules and

Side Note 8.
- Shackleton and his *Endurance* Party had two opportunities to adhere to biophysical reality and avoid catastrophe.
- One, purchase a round bottomed ship like the *Fram* rather than the *Endurance*.
- Two, follow the advice of South Georgian whalers and delay the expedition until conditions were less severe in the Weddell Sea.

understandings of the natural sciences, including human nature, the greater the likelihood of creating durable societies.

Natural scientists have discovered much about the workings of the natural world by adhering to a unity of knowledge espoused in the Enlightenment several hundred years ago. Of course, our quest will never be complete with some phenomena not yielding to scientific inquiry. We just don't know which ones will remain ever obscure.

Consider biology. Foremost, nothing we know about living systems violates the fundamentals of chemistry or physics. An organism, be it a bacterium or an elephant, is composed of atoms that are composed of even more elemental units that follow the rules of chemistry and physics. Each level of organization is founded on others of finer scale. This is the way science has organized verifiable evidence in order to understand the natural world.

The discipline of thermodynamics describes how a series of rules or laws governs the transformations of energy. Simply said, the first law states that energy can neither be created nor destroyed but can change form. The second law states that useful energy—the capacity to do work—decreases whenever an energy conversion occurs. These rules apply to living and nonliving systems alike. For example, the useful work that steam can do is less than that in the coal that we use to convert water to steam. Likewise, the work your muscles can do when fueled with a spoonful of sugar is less than that possible for the chemical energy contained in that amount of sugar. Rules that govern behavior in elements and molecules also apply to organisms. Similarly, the behavior of organisms is subject to the fundamental principles of chemistry and physics, and is explainable—at least in principle—in physical and chemical terms.

We have not discerned the biological rules that govern living systems from the principles of physics and chemistry, although biology is consistent with the rules of these disciplines. The cell theory—all cells are derived from preexisting cells (except the "first" cell)—is an emergent property of life. That is, an emergent property is greater than or at least different from the properties of the component parts—a cell has new properties that are not expressed by the individual aggregates of molecules or the various organelles—mitochondrion, chloroplast, nucleus, centriole, vacuole—that make up a cell. Consider a simple example: the properties of water (H_2O)—freezing and boiling temperatures, for instance—are not the properties of its component elements (O: oxygen and H: hydrogen). They emerge as a function of the particular ways in which oxygen and hydrogen atoms combine to form water molecules. In like manner the principles and rules of genetics, development, physiology, ecology, evolution, and behavior are emergent properties of organisms and their associations with each other and the physical world.

With the evolution of social vertebrates and then, some 70,000 years ago, of behaviorally modern *Homo sapiens* as the presence of symbolic art at their camps indicated, a whole new set of emergent properties appeared: abstract thought, self-awareness, complex symbolic language, music, art, spirituality and the capacity to believe virtually anything imaginable, to name a few. For much of our existence as social animals we lived in small groups of hunter-gatherers. We did not know how most of the world worked. Actually, it was hidden from us. Our senses do not detect, for example, radio waves, gamma radiation, atoms, or hormones. With sensory inputs alone, we are unable to explain the development of a hand or a flower, or the formation of Earth because explanations for such things are far beyond our experienced world. However, with the emergence of abstract thought, self awareness, and language we became capable of explaining life's mysteries with imagined stories made believable by our capacity to envision alternative realities.

The modern human brain, as a product of evolution, has been built upon ancestral brains as Reg Morrison, a photo-journalist and writer, describes:

> [T]he brain is often spoken of as though it were an architect-designed, fully integrated unit, rather like a computer—but one generally driven by novices and idiots. The human brain in reality is more like an old farmhouse, a crude patchwork of lean-tos and other extensions that conceal entirely the ancient amphibian-reptilian toolshed at its core. That it works at all should be cause for wonderment. As for pointing to our mental failures with scorn or dismay, we might as well profess disappointment with the mechanics of gravity … In other words, the degree of disillusionment we feel in response to any particular human behavior is the precise measure of our ignorance of its evolutionary and genetic origins.

The brain is fundamentally an emotional organ that can reason and employ logic but the amphibian-reptilian elements are primary. Integrated with the rest of the body via numerous hormones and other signaling molecules, it is responsive to all manner of environmental inputs via the body's sensory systems. The body-mind system is a single functional unit, hard-wired for survival and behaviors that promote reproduction. As a result of its evolutionary origin, the brain's elements are not in lock-step; rather, often in conflict. Each person is unique in behavior, in large part, because every brain is different not only in subtle features of neuronal wiring and construction but also in the environmental inputs that have programmed it.

Over the last century and a half, we used the powerful lens of Darwinian evolution to visualize our biological history and the role natural selection played in producing the diversity of life. The rules of natural selection are simple. When a trait is heritable and endows its possessor with an even slightly elevated survival probability, the individual is more likely to reproduce more progeny than an individual without the trait. Over time the trait will become more common; in some cases expressed by all individuals in an interbreeding population. Most, if not all, of the traits expressed by an organism have been naturally selected in an organism's ancestors, all the way back to the first cell. Nevertheless, the current function of a behavior or structure may not reflect the initial function upon which selection pressure acted—feathers were not initially selected for flight but rather for other functions, perhaps insulation or coloration. Biologists call this process exaptation, the evolution of an old structure or behavior for a new function.

Evolution is the uniting concept of biology without which nothing about life makes sense. *Homo sapiens* evolved to be a fantasy-inspired, omnivorous, territorial, tribal mammal with language that can create complex cultures. These behavioral traits, despite our physical weaknesses, have enabled our kind to colonize numerous islands and every continent except Antarctica. At the same time, because of how evolution works, humanity must overcome two barriers to a bright future: 1) the tendency to believe anything even without credible evidence and 2) natural selection acts in the present with no anticipation of future conditions.

The capacity to believe almost anything is fundamental to human nature. It likely evolved because the ability to believe strongly gave the individual with this tendency survival advantage. Consider two thought experiments. Experiment 1: Condition A. You believe to the point of total exhaustion, even death, that you can do something—climb a mountain, become the fastest runner in your region, subdue an attacking lion. Condition B. You believe that you might be able to do something, but not to the point of exhaustion or death. Other things being equal, under what conditions are you most likely to succeed? It is easy to accept that having the capacity to believe strongly has selective advantage in accomplishing something of great difficulty or what might even appear impossible. This capacity to believe strongly was a critical element in the *Endurance* Party's survival.

Experiment 2: Condition A. In your group, hunters cooperate by contributing to the common good that which each individual does best, thereby largely eliminating competition. Condition B. In your group, hunters seldom cooperate but compete to make the kill. All else being equal, under what conditions will your group most likely make a kill, and thereby improve the group's survival potential? Clearly, cooperative behavior among group members gives the group a selective advantage over less cooperative groups. It is easy to accept that a propensity to believe strongly, combined with the capacity to cooperate, helped our ancestors to survive on the African savannas and eventually disperse across much of the planet. Evidence indicates that spirituality (religion) came into existence because it fostered greater group cooperation.

We know that humans tend to form closely knit groups, and that within a group individuals often act altruistically rather than selfishly. Experts don't agree on how altruistic behavior evolved, but group selection—selecting the behaviors of individuals that favored their group's success but not necessarily survival of the actors—played a major role. Altruism is absolutely essential to remedy humanity's most threatening environmental challenges: climate change, extinction of species and ecosystems, loss of life support, overpopulation, excessive consumption, resource depletion, and a dysfunctional economic system.

Many people cling to previously discredited explanations of the natural world. For example, the majority of people in the United States do not accept that evolution explains the diversity of life, including our species. Recognizing that our propensity to believe almost anything is based in genetics means that this tendency can't be easily suppressed. This is one of those inconvenient constraints imposed by our evolutionary history, one that makes it difficult for billions of people to accept the use of scientific knowledge in making important decisions. Why is this true for so many people? First, most cultures instruct their members to believe alternative explanations. Second, we did not evolve to think in terms of biology, physics, or other evidence-based disciplines. Third, the rules and understandings of these sciences are usually abstract, often not intuitively grasped, and hard won.

Consider one especially compelling example. Modern humans required 70,000 years to discover deoxyribonucleic acid (DNA) and until 1953 to determine that, although consisting of just four nucleotide subunits (adenine, cytosine, guanine, thymine), this molecule codes genetic information.

The second conundrum we face is that Darwinian evolution can only act in the present. That is, heritable change results from current selection pressure. As a result, human behaviors that we now express are, by and large, those that had proved successful in the past. Consequently, some elements of behavior today are maladaptive because they hark back to past contexts and challenges. Edward O. Wilson, an eminent evolutionary biologist, eloquently summarizes humanity's predicament:

> The relative indifference to the environment springs, I believe, from deep within human nature. The human brain evidently evolved to commit itself emotionally only to a small piece of geography, a limited band of kinsmen, and two or three generations into the future. To look neither far ahead nor far afield is elemental in a Darwinian sense. We are innately inclined to ignore any distant possibility not yet requiring examination. It is, people say, just good common sense. Why do they think in this short-sighted way? The reason is simple: it is a hard-wired part of our Paleolithic heritage. For hundreds of millennia those who worked for short-term gain within a small circle of relatives and friends lived longer and left more offspring—even when their collective striving caused their chiefdoms and empires to crumble around them. The long view that might have saved their distant descendants required a vision and extended altruism instinctively difficult to marshal.

We will have to overcome this evolutionary legacy by prompting culturally reinforced vision and altruism that fosters actions today that lead to enduring societies in the future. For example, we shall have to devise ways to curtail emissions of heat-trapping gases to avoid evermore climate instability and to ensure that our descendants have climates conducive to human habitation.

Seven billion humans clearly constitute the most powerful of the biological agents that constantly drive Darwinian evolution on the planet. The changes we have wrought by our activities are creating a planet for which we are not adapted. Global civilization's very survival is now dependent upon humankind employing what the natural sciences and other evidence-based disciplines have taught us to resolve our environmental challenges.

CHAPTER 8

Climate Change

The Weddell Sea Party endured nature at its worst: blizzards, snow, ice, cold, and hundred-mile-per-hour winds on land and at sea, as well as 200-foot waves, powerful currents and rip tides. In effect, they survived some of the cruelest weather conditions imaginable. A century later, our planet is experiencing unprecedented human-driven climate change. As the coming decades and centuries unfold, the weather in many places will likely rival in severity that which Elephant Island and the Drake Passage delivered to Shackleton and his men. However, it will not be cold, but hot extremes and associated weather anomalies.

For millennia, humans have been altering local climates, sometimes sufficient to undo their society. Evidence indicating the possibility that we could radically alter global climate goes back to 1896 when the Swedish chemist Svante Arrhenius showed that doubling the CO_2 concentration in the atmosphere would warm the planet several degrees Fahrenheit, a number similar to that which climate models in the latter part of the 20th century predicted.

Climate science took another major step forward in 1958 when atmospheric CO_2 monitoring began atop Mauna Loa on the island of Hawaii. The resulting record, known as the Keeling Curve in honor of Charles Keeling, who initiated the measurements, established that atmospheric CO_2 has increased over the past 55 years from 315 parts per million (ppm) to 400 ppm in 2013, an increase of 27 percent. The Keeling Curve also established that the rate of increase has more than doubled from 1 ppm/year at mid-20th century to over 2 ppm/year today. If we reduced the rate of this human-caused increase to 2 ppm/year, we would reach 570 ppm by 2100. If only 1 ppm/year, it would be 480 ppm. However, if we merely stopped the acceleration in CO_2 release in the next decade, it would be a major accomplishment. Unfortunately, if we fail to turndown the Keeling Curve's slope soon,

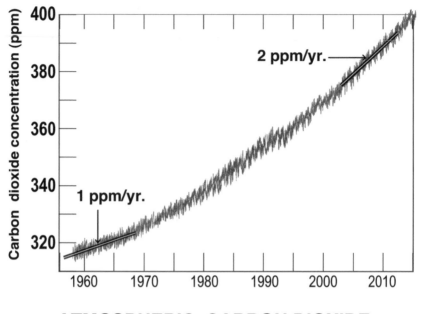

ATMOSPHERIC CARBON DIOXIDE

8.1: The Keeling Curve of atmospheric CO_2 concentration atop Mauna Loa exhibits an accelerating rate of increase over the past 55 years. Saw tooth pattern is from seasonal variation in CO_2 uptake via photosynthesis. The larger land mass in the northern hemisphere takes up more CO_2 (its summer, down line), than the smaller land mass of the southern hemisphere (its summer, up line).

global mean temperature will continue to rise rapidly, thereby prompting ever greater climate instability.

Every week scientific publications present data consistent with the onset of climate instability caused by increased heat-trapping gases which human activities generate. James Hansen, one of the world's eminent climate scientists, recently published a paper that definitively establishes more hot summers around the globe. He writes, "We can say with a high degree of confidence that events such as the extreme summer heat in the Moscow region in 2010 and Texas in 2011 were a consequence of global warming."

What is remarkable about Hansen's results in 2012 is that a paper he and colleagues published in 1988 foreshadowed what he affirmed in the 2012 paper. Hansen writes in the 2012 paper:

> "Loading" of the climate dice is one way to describe a systematic shift of temperature anomalies. [In the 1988 paper we] repre-

Side Note 9.

- Humanity had two scientific warnings to level the slope of the Keeling curve, thereby lessening the likelihood of climate instability.
- The first came from Arrhenius' calculations and the initial rise in CO_2 concentration during the early part of the last century.
- The second came from the Keeling Curve's upward slope which scientists first observed in the 1960s.

sented the climate of 1951-1980 by colored dice with two sides colored red for "hot", two sides blue for "cold", and two sides white for near average temperatures. With a normal distribution of anomalies the dividing points are $\pm 0.43\sigma$ to achieve equal (one third) chances for each of these three categories in the base period (1951-1980). [Note: σ stands for standard deviation that is a measure of variability in a data set.]

[A climate model was] used to project how the odds would change due to global warming for alternative greenhouse gas scenarios. Scenario B, which had climate forcing that turned out to be very close to reality, led to four of the dice sides being red early in the 21st century based on climate model simulations. ...

[Data in the 2012 paper] reveals that the occurrence of "hot" summers (seasonal mean temperature anomaly exceeding $+0.43\sigma$) has reached the level of 67 [percent] required to make four sides of the dice red in both the Northern Hemisphere and Southern Hemisphere. ... [Odds are equal for an unusually cool season or an average season with each corresponding to approximately one side of the six-sided dice.]

Probably the most important change is the emergence of a new category of "extremely hot" summers, more than 3σ [3 standard deviations] warmer than the base period. [The data] illustrate that $+3\sigma$ anomalies practically did not exist in 1951-1980, but in the past several years these extreme anomalies have covered of the order of 10 [percent] of the land area.

Consistent with this remarkable worldwide increase in extremely hot summers were the temperatures in Australia in January 2013 (southern hemisphere summer). Six days during that month ranked among the hottest

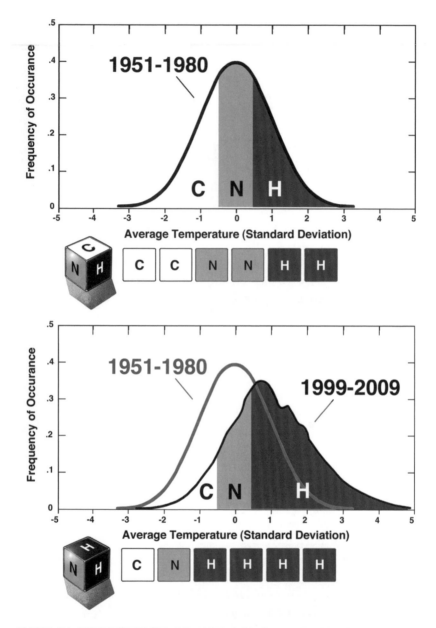

SHIFT IN DISTRIBUTION OF AVERAGE SUMMER TEMERATURES

8.2: Distribution of summer temperatures for 1951 to 1980 and 1999 to 2009 illustrating a shift to significantly hotter summers in the second time period. This shift is depicted as "climate dice" where the probability has gone from two in six chances of a hot, normal, or cool summer in 1951 to 1980 to four in six chances of a hot summer and one in six chances for a cool or normal summer in 1999 to 2009.

20 days in Australia since 1910 when records began. January 7 set the national average maximum at 40.33°C (104.6° F), besting the previous record of 40.17° C (104.3° F) set on December 21, 1972. During January 2013, temperature maximums across the continent ranged from 40° C to 48° C (104° F to 118° F). Much of Australia experienced new highs—temperatures reached close to 48° C (118° F) in an area in South Australia the size of the island province of Tasmania. This exceptional period of high temperatures led the Australian Bureau of Meteorology to add two new colors to its weather forecasting chart: deep purple for 50° C to 52° C (122° F to 126° F) and pink for 52° C to 54° C (126° F to 129° F).

Hansen and colleagues' data establish that climate change is upon us and foreshadow the coming of a much warmer climate driven by CO_2 levels that now exceed those prevailing at any time in the past million years. Our future climate will be radically different from the one for which human societies were designed and to which the natural world is adapted.

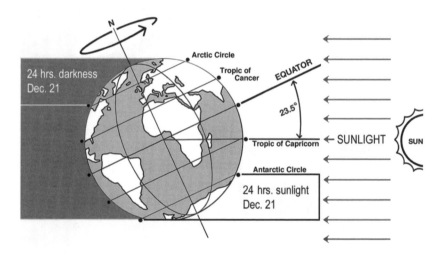

8.3: The seasons, day lengths, and climate experienced at a particular place are, in large part, a result of Earth being tipped 23.5° on its axis of rotation relative to the plain of its orbit around the sun. In the diagram, the northern hemisphere is in winter and the North Pole has 24 hours of darkness while the South Pole has 24 hours of light. Also, days are shorter in the northern hemisphere and colder, the opposite of the southern hemisphere. Equatorial regions over the year receive more direct sunlight than more southern or northern regions, thus more energy per unit area. For this reason equatorial regions are warmer than other parts of the globe. Simplistically, it is the equalization of these energy-temperature differences that produce weather and different climates.

Arresting Climate Change

By the late 1960s the Keeling curve was sufficiently developed to demonstrate that atmospheric CO_2 was rising rapidly and already about 40 ppm higher than during the late 19th century, an increase of 15 percent. Based on Arrhenius's calculations that raising CO_2 would increase Earth's temperature, we were well on the way to doubling CO_2 levels, which would warm the planet by at least several degrees. We clearly knew by the mid-1970s that doubling the CO_2 levels to 560 ppm would have drastic climate consequences. Adding globally 4 watts of retained heat per square meter of surface is huge—almost a 2 percent increase from 240 watts per square meter in 1900. By the late 1980s, climate science was well enough established to inspire Bill McKibben, an accomplished non-fiction writer, to author *The End of Nature*, the first general audience book highlighting the serious threat posed by elevating CO_2 in the atmosphere.

Climate scientist, Stephen Schneider, predicted in 1976, "I do believe, however, that if concentrations of CO_2, and perhaps aerosols, continue to increase, demonstrable climatic changes could occur by the end of this century, if not sooner." In 1988, climate scientist Hansen made three points in his testimony before the United States Congress:

> Number one, the earth is warmer in 1988 than at any time in the history of instrumental measurements [with 99 percent confidence]. Number two, the global warming is now large enough that we can ascribe with a high degree of confidence a cause and effect relationship to the greenhouse effect. And number three, our computer climate simulations indicate that the greenhouse effect is already large enough to begin to affect the probability of extreme events such as summer heat waves."

The United Nations Environmental Programme and the World Meteorological Organization founded the Intergovernmental Panel on Climate Change (IPCC) in 1988 in recognition of the importance of climate change for humans. Its staff—comprised of 2,500 technical experts representing the disciplines of climatology, ecology, economics, medicine, and oceanography from 60 countries—was charged with coordinating and periodically reporting scientific information on climate change and its implications. As scientific evidence mounted, a consensus emerged among climate scientists and others: human activities were forcing a rapid warming. At the same time, for a variety of reasons, many others uncomfortable with the scientific forecasts advocated for continued dependence on fossil-fuel based energy.

Business leaders—especially those with vested interests in continued reliance on fossil fuels—and numerous economists provided assessments, based upon economic arguments, concluding that addressing climate change would be too expensive. The fault line separating the advocates for aggressive reduction of heat trapping gas emissions versus those who counseled little or no action was between ecologically oriented biologists and mainstream economists. Biologists were primarily concerned about the likely devastating effects of climate extremes on biodiversity and the future of civilization as we know it. Few economists could say the same. These two groups had radically different worldviews based on what each knew and believed to be the most important reality: nature's rules versus human-created economics.

Among businesses only the insurance industry, whose payouts for natural disasters were dramatically rising, began to accept the reality of climate change. During the 1990s, a coalition of fossil fuel companies, politically conservative think tanks, foundations, and wealthy individuals initiated a massive disinformation campaign that continues today. Its objective? To raise doubt among the general public about the reliability of climate science. They have succeeded in spades. In 1997 a Democrat-controlled United States Senate voted 97 to 0 not to ratify the Kyoto Protocol, an international initiative of the IPCC designed to reduce CO_2 emissions. Currently, a majority in the United States House of Representatives believes climate change is a hoax—or at least publicly proclaims so. In the past 15 years, contenders in most state and national elections in the United States have ignored climate change. In fact, the contenders in the most recent United States presidential and vice presidential election debates never mentioned it. It had become another third rail of national elections—touch it and you're politically dead. Modest change, however, may be coming. President Barack Obama pledged in his 2013 Inaugural and State of the Union addresses to put climate change on the agenda in his second term. Unfortunately, without vigorous national and international initiatives to drastically reduce emissions, climate instability will proceed apace.

Based on paleoclimatology, climate scientists have warned that we should not exceed 350 ppm for long because of the substantial associated warming and the changes that warming will bring. If we do exceed 450 ppm, the resulting warming will likely trigger positive feedback mechanisms that will result in even higher CO_2 levels thereby exacerbating consequences: 1) all high mountain and polar glaciers will melt, causing sea levels to rise perhaps more than 200 hundred feet and melting of Antarctic ice will likely change totally ocean circulation ushering in new climates everywhere, 2) carbon now sequestered in frozen tundra soils in the northern hemisphere will be released, 3) methane (another potent heat-trapping gas) will release from frozen soils and from methylclathrates, frozen methane-ice compounds in ocean bottoms—thereby warming the atmosphere even more, rendering massive climate change unavoidable.

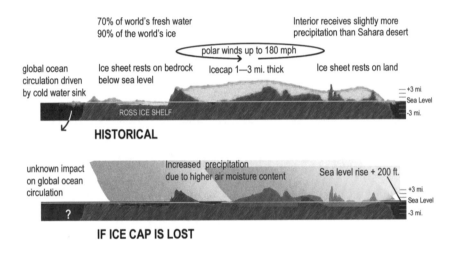

8.4: Depiction of the historical state of Antarctic ice and sea level contrasted to an altered state if all of Antarctica's ice cap melted. The climate of Antarctica would warm and exhibit significantly increased precipitation. Global ocean circulation would radically change in ways unknowable resulting in different climates everywhere.

Climate scientists have clearly established that human activities have increased significantly the atmosphere's heat-trapping capacity, thereby prompting the onset of climate instability and a hotter planet. At this time, humanity has not used these climate findings to properly address what was pending in the 1970s, but is now confirmed global warming. What we do to rapidly drop atmospheric CO_2 concentration toward 350 ppm to avoid more climate change than is already here and in the offing will determine the character of life on Earth.

CHAPTER 9

Biodiversity and Life Support

Seals, sea leopards, and penguins may appear to have been sufficient to provide much of the fuel and food required by the *Endurance* Party. However, without fish these animals would have starved, as would fish without plankton. Shackleton and his men were, in fact, utterly dependent upon the entire Weddell Sea ecosystem and what the *Endurance* Party had brought with them—humans cannot survive in Antarctica without imports.

The activities of an ever-growing population of humans is forcing climate change, destroying natural habitats, introducing alien species, and causing pollution and over-harvesting, thereby eliminating species and impoverishing ecosystems critical for all life. Appropriate concentrations of atmospheric gases, stable ocean temperatures and acidity, fertile soil, clean water, food and nutrients, waste disposal, diversity of species and complexity of ecosystems are all essential elements to support life.

If extinctions continue to increase, humans will end up responsible for the greatest biocatastrophe since the extinction of dinosaurs 65 million years ago caused, in large part, by a meteor impact. Based on past mass extinctions, the ecosphere will then enter a several-million-year period of instability. The probability of civilization surviving even the early phases of this period of upheaval is nil, similar to that of the *Endurance* Party if spring had not brought back the large predators.

Most people view biodiversity simply as species richness or the kinds of organisms that inhabit a particular place. Yes, the number of species a place harbors is a measure of biodiversity for that place. Nonetheless, biodiversity encompasses far more—the variety observed in DNA and protein composition all the way to that in ecosystems and biomes as well as the interactions among all these elements. It is the functioning of this diversity that creates life support for everything.

A useful way to appreciate the importance of biodiversity is to imagine what you need to stay alive and healthy, and its source. Oxygen: photosynthetic bacteria and green plants break the chemical bonds in water and release oxygen as a byproduct. External heat and energy from the sun: cellular biochemistry (metabolism) falters and then fails much outside the temperature range of 32° to 212° thereby requiring an atmosphere that retains just the right amount of solar heat. Water vapor and CO_2 are the major heat-trapping gases that make Earth habitable. Plants withdraw innumerable tons of CO_2 from the atmosphere via photosynthesis while transpiring vast amounts of water into the air. Nearly all organisms release CO_2 and water as they use the photosynthetically acquired energy that powers virtually all organisms.

Humans cannot make all the amino acids necessary to synthesize proteins (major structural components of cells and tissues, as well as enzymes that are the catalysts of metabolism in organisms) and for that we need plant or animal tissues that contain these essential amino acids. Also, we cannot synthesize certain vitamins. We get some of these vitamins from bacteria living in our intestines and others from various organisms we eat. We use medicines to cure illnesses and otherwise stay healthy, most of which come from microorganisms, plants, and animals. For flood control and potable water, forests and wetlands do an excellent job.

You and all other organisms generate waste and dead bodies. Bacteria, fungi, insects, and other invertebrates do what human societies need to do: reuse and recycle everything!

We've considered physical needs, but humans have emotional and spiritual needs too. The presence of green plants can be emotionally calming and beneficial, as is interacting with animals. Human history is replete with spiritual affiliations with various organisms. Biophilia, or love of life, is innate—part of human nature.

Earth alone provides the resources humans and other life require. Through most of human history they were free for the taking. Now, we have to create technological solutions to provide life support functions that our activities have compromised. Five hundred years ago in the Americas, water in most streams was potable, the level of toxic chemicals in the soil and air poisoned few if any organisms, and the majority of people practiced living off the land. Today, most of Earth's 7 billion people do not live off the land, water purification and waste treatment plants abound,

9.1: Meteorologist Hussey hugging sled dog Samson illustrating biophilia, or the love of life, a feature of human nature.

and the world has tens of thousands of toxic waste sites that require cleanup—we can't clean polluted aquifers. It will require perhaps centuries to purge any contaminate.

Behaviorally modern *Homo sapiens* walked out of Africa some 70,000 years ago to colonize most of the rest of the planet. For the most part, we do not know the repercussions of our early migrations and colonizations; however, our impact on native species was often cataclysmic. On our arrival in what were to become the Americas, Australia, Madagascar, and New Zealand, we hunted and otherwise pushed to extinction the majority of the mega faunas—large animals—inhabiting these places.

The loss of many birds endemic to the Hawaiian Islands is typical of human-caused extinctions. After Polynesians colonized these Pacific islands in about 1250 CE, 60 species of land birds became extinct. Of the remaining 50 species, 17 disappeared following the arrival of Europeans. Similar patterns apply elsewhere. In Australia European settlers caused the extinction of 16 mammal species and another 34 are red-listed by the International Union for Conservation of Nature (IUCN) as vulnerable, endangered, or critically endangered. Australia is thus positioned to lose another 20 percent of its native mammals unless humans significantly reduce their ecologically destructive activities.

Europeans first arrived in the Americas more than 500 years ago. As on many islands, in 1844 a flightless bird was the first recorded extinction. The elimination of about 450 more species in the United States followed the demise of the great auk (*Pinguinus impennis*). Extensive analyses published in 2000 characterized the status of 20,897 species of animals and plants in the United States: 6,460, or 31 percent, are critically imperiled, imperiled, or vulnerable. A full one-third of the vascular plants fall into one of these categories. This is most disturbing, because vascular plants are the foundational base for most ecosystems, acquiring the majority of their energy, and constituting the bulk of the biomass.

It is important to note that more than half of species known to science are insects. They are invaluable to the planet's health, yet we have neither count of species nor a complete assessment of their roles in ecosystems. Wilson sums up their relevance: "So important are insects and other land-dwelling arthropods that if all were to disappear, humanity probably could not last more than a few months." The same is true for bacteria and other microorganisms. It is the little creatures that provide planetary wellbeing, yet we know too little about them or our influence on them.

The latest Red List of the IUCN describes the status in 2008 of the world's 5,488 mammalian species: some 1,200 of which, or 22 percent, are threatened, with habitat loss posing the greatest threat, and utilization, or use by humans, coming in second. Brian Czech, a wildlife conservation biologist, used the documented reasons for listing a species on the United States Endangered Species List to establish that only 1 of the 877 species listed in 1995 was not impacted by humans—the Florida salt marsh vole (*Microtus pennsylvanicus dukecampbelli*). Czech wrote:

[My analysis attributed endangered status to] urbanization, agriculture, outdoor recreations and tourism, domestic livestock and ranching activities, reservoirs and other water diversions, modified fire regimes, pollution, mineral/oil/gas exploration and extraction, logging, industrial development, roads, aquifer depletion, and a few other causes ... This "Who's Who" of the American economy ... comprises the economic context of the Endangered Species Act.

Conserving Biodiversity and the Life Support It Provides

It's likely that our ancestors attempted conservation efforts prior to recorded history. More recently some indigenous peoples forbade hunting in breeding grounds, while others had cultural restrictions that influenced when and how many animals or plants people could harvest. Slash and burn agriculturalists traveled place-to-place, disturbing only small patches of land that, for the most part, returned to their original condition when abandoned. Nomadic herders had cultural patterns of migration that preserved the ecosystems on which they depended. Early agriculturalists developed crop rotation and methods of soil enrichment—animal bodies and manure as well as plant material. At the same time, the number of people was small compared to resources. For example, although native North Americans in the southwest drove more bison than they could use to their deaths over cliffs, the fecundity of millions easily replaced those killed. It took the arrival of train transportation and Americans with rifles killing bison for leather and meat to reduce the number from some 30 million to a mere 1,000 and near extinction.

We know now that the indigenous peoples' efforts to preserve biological resources were but gestures because their overall impact on the diversity of life was significant as observed in the pre-modern extinction records considered above. Nevertheless, the overall influence on the environment was limited because of small populations and primitive technologies. We can observe more recent human impacts from space. We know from science that within just a few hundred years humans have radically changed Earth's surface, warmed the oceans, altered the atmosphere, and significantly reduced biodiversity. Consider two of numerous examples. Vast numbers of land-clearing fires and logging roads are visible to satellites showing the constant reduction of Amazonian rainforest. The Aral Sea in 1960 was the fourth largest lake in the world (26,250 square miles). Today its area is decreased by half and its volume is down 75 percent—equivalent to draining two United States Great Lakes: Erie and Ontario. The fishing industry has collapsed and local climate is hotter and dryer in summer, colder in

Side Note 10.

- Some humans have known for at least 2,000 years that their activities impoverished biodiversity and life support on a local scale.
- By the second half of the last century the verifiable evidence was overwhelming as to our global devastation of life and the negative consequences thereby realized.
- We are now entering the sixth mass extinction.

winter. These changes and many others are happening too rapidly thereby causing ecosystems to unravel.

Large-scale conservation and restoration efforts have become ever more common since the late 19th century as we have come to understand just how devastating human activities have been, and are, both locally and globally. European settlers in the United States had clear cut the Adirondack Mountains in upstate New York by the latter part of the 19th century, resulting in massive flooding along the Hudson River. In response, the Sacandaga River was dammed to create the Great Sacandaga Lake for flood control. At the same time, the "forever wild" amendment to the New York State Constitution in 1894 established the Adirondack Park, 600 million acres of public and private land, to protect and allow the area ravaged by logging to reforest.

The United States government established Yellowstone National Park on March 1, 1872, followed in 1890 by Sequoia and Yosemite national parks. Today, the National Park Service has 401 areas comprising 84 million acres and the National Forest Service has 155 units with 188 million acres. Together they represent about 11 percent of the land area of the United States. The total size of all protected areas—federal, state, tribal and local level authorities—comprises over 1 million square miles. This is 27 percent of United States land area and one-tenth of the protected areas in the world. The reasons for protecting most of these areas were several: unique spectacular landscapes and special features such as hot springs in the national parks; preservation of timber and grazing lands in the national forests; and recreational use. Interestingly, comprehensive biodiversity and life support preservation were not the primary incentives for establishing the national parks and forests, but rather serendipitous outcomes.

Twentieth century concern for birds and other wildlife prompted the emergence of a wide range of national and international organizations including Audubon, Conservation International, Green Peace, Natural Resources Defense Council, Oceana, Sierra Club, The Nature Conservancy, Wildlife Conservation Society, and World Wildlife Fund. Thousands of local land trusts and conservancies have joined these groups, all striving to reverse the persistent human-wrought impoverishment of biodiversity.

The Endangered Species Act of 1973 passed 390 to 12 in the United States House of Representatives and 92 to 0 in the Senate. It was a bold law that provided rights for species other than humans thereby attempting to correct an unfortunate omission in the United States Constitution and Bill of Rights that permitted their extinction. At the time, preservation efforts focused on species rather than on communities, ecosystems, or biomes because we could identify endangered species and know their habitat needs.

Other conservation perspectives were also emerging. One recognizes the importance of setting aside millions of acres of wilderness in which ecological and evolutionary processes could play out largely free from human influence. Another perspective is based on the understanding that species do not exist in isolation but require complex interactions with, and dependencies on, a host of other species as well as unique physical and chemical conditions for their populations to persist and not dwindle to extinction. Yet another approach employs the observation that intact native ecosystems that harbor robust populations of top predators are healthy. The presence of top predators is indicative of a stable functional ecosystem because constellations of species, communities, and habitats are necessary to support viable populations of predators.

Dave Foreman, conservationist and champion of wilderness, and colleagues conceived the Wildlands Project, now the Wildlands Network, in the 1980s. Then, with others, they initiated in the 1990s their audacious vision for preserving and enhancing biodiversity on a continental scale. The organization embodies the above perspectives derived from conservation biology. Its long-term goal is to return half the North American continent to wildlands with functional ecosystems, complete with top predators, where ecological and evolutionary processes play out relatively unencumbered.

The Wildlands Network works with many conservation organizations and other like minded groups on myriad pieces of land to create a connected wilderness area that runs up the continental divide from Mexico to the Arctic Circle with a loop that includes Baja California, the Coastal Range, and the Sierras, and that connects to mountainous protected areas in northwestern United States and Canada. The organization is designing a similar network to run from Florida through the Appalachian Mountains to Maine and then to Nova Scotia, with a side branch across the northeastern forest from Maine to the Adirondack Park in upstate New York and north into Algonquin Park in Canada. An east-west network across Canada and parts of the northern United States to connect the eastern and western networks is in the planning stages. When complete, this continental network of core wilderness and compatible-use areas connected by corridors will enable many North American species to live as they once did and to migrate freely, unhindered by human activities to the greatest degree possible.

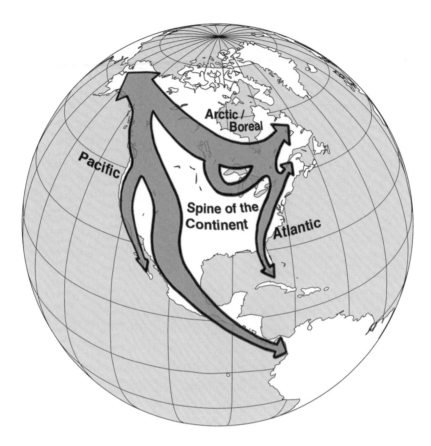

9.2: Schematic map of the proposed wildlands corridors for North America.

Of all of the mega challenges before humanity the degradation of our planet's life support capacity is unique because it is invisible to most people. Life support is just there, like homeostasis in our bodies—appropriate pH, oxygen and sugar levels in our blood; secretion of digestive enzymes; removal of toxins by the liver—and only noticed when disrupted. Additionally, in human time the degradation proceeds slowly. It takes one or two lifetimes to note the passage.

Aldo Leopold, the noted wildlife biologist, and his brother visited and explored the Colorado River delta by canoe in 1922. Leopold wrote:

When the sun peeped over the Sierra Madre, it slanted across a hundred miles of lovely desolation, a vast flat bowl of wilderness rimmed by jagged peaks. On the map the Delta was bisected by the river, but in fact the river was nowhere and everywhere, for he [the river] could not decide which of a hundred green lagoons offered the most pleasant and least speedy path to the Gulf.

Leopold then recalls:

"He leadeth me by still waters" was to us only a phrase in a book until we nosed our canoe through the green lagoons. ... A verdant wall of mesquite and willow separated the channel from the thorny desert beyond. At each bend we saw egrets standing in the pools ahead, ... Fleets of cormorants drove their black prows in quest of skittering mullets; avocets, willets, and yellow-legs dozed one-legged on the bars; mallards, widgeons, and teal sprang skyward in alarm. ... When a troop of egrets settled on a far green willow, they looked like a premature snowstorm.

Sandra Postel, world expert on freshwater, wrote in 2012:

Today, the Colorado delta is a shadow of its former self. Once one of the planet's most vital aquatic ecosystems, it is now one of the most threatened. A low-altitude flight over the region reveals a desiccated landscape of salt flats and cracked earth. There is little sign of a living river because the river is gone; in all but the wettest years, it disappears into the desert sands a short distance south of the border.

The hundred year story of the Colorado River delta is merely one of innumerable cuts bleeding biodiversity dry. Most go unnoticed, proceeding unabated.

CHAPTER 10

Human Population

The Weddell Sea Party did not have a population problem; however, had it been larger success would have been less likely. Demographers predict our current population will grow by a few billion before settling or falling. Populations always decrease when they exceed the carrying capacity of their habitats, whether by fouling their habitat, diminishing essential resources, or both. The rules of ecology and population dynamics oblige this fate. Humans are governed by this given that is not negotiable despite alternative realities the human brain can conjure and believe.

In the last 100,000 years, human population grew from no more than 100,000 to 1 billion in 1800. It is now more than 7 billion, just 200 years later. From a biological perspective, unlimited growth is hard wired into all organisms and curtailed by resource limitations. In the short term modern humanity has avoided resource limits. At the same time, our brains have enabled us to appreciate the power of exponential population and consumption growth to overwhelm a finite system. Unfortunately, this fact is either unknown to, or unappreciated by, most everybody. Perhaps this ignorance persists because the purported metric is our extraordinary biological success measured in number of people and habitat creation. At the same time, it is sobering to realize that no population of an animal species that weighs more than 110 pounds has ever reached 7 billion—our population anomaly will correct itself.

Organisms exhibit a variety of population growth patterns, but many present one of two extreme patterns that tends to correlate with a particular set of characteristics. The r-selected species are usually small in size and have many offspring, but invest little energy in them. They mature quickly and have a short life expectancy. They reproduce exponentially in order to exploit the brief periods of favorable conditions that occur between the frequent disturbances that characterize unstable habitats—a boom-bust pattern. We find typical r-selected organisms like bacteria, slime molds, algae, and rodents in seasonally affected bodies of water, flood plains, and tilled fields. K-selected organisms are usually large but have few offspring, to which they invest substantial energy. The organisms mature slowly, have a long life expectancy, and live in stable environments such as mature forests, savannas, and grass lands. Their growth curves exhibit exponential growth that levels off near the carrying capacity of a particular place. Deer, moose, grizzly bears, and elephants are typical K-type organisms. Humans fit the characteristics of K-selected organisms best in all respects except for growth pattern—our population size has not leveled off based on the carrying capacity of our global habitat.

Are humans exceptional because we are not habitat limited, or are we unique in having a boom-bust pattern that has not yet boomed-out—as has occurred with some isolated human populations? Two centuries ago, Thomas Malthus's *Essay on the Principle of Population* predicted that disease,

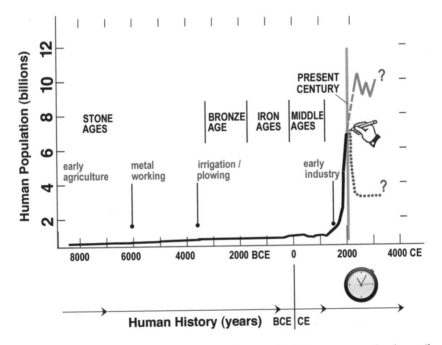

10.1: The global human population over the past 10,000 years grew slowly until less than a thousand years ago when its rate of growth accelerated reaching a rate of almost a billion every decade in the 1960s. The future pattern of growth is unpredictable; however, the current rate will decrease in the future.

Side Note 11.

- Malthus provided two centuries ago the clarion call on the power of exponential growth to overwhelm planetary life support capacity.
- Aldo Leopold and Rachael Carson in the middle of the last century provided evidence of large scale degradation of life support functions.
- Ehrlich and others followed with even more details in the 1960s, about the time our numbers exceeded what some contend to be Earth's human carrying capacity.

starvation, resource shortages, civil strife, and war would reduce our population size if we didn't do it ourselves. It didn't happen in the way or at the time that Malthus predicted. *The Population Bomb*, written in 1968 by Paul Ehrlich, an eminent ecologist, cautioned similarly. Again, we have not realized the consequences as predicted. Why? Simply put, human ingenuity prevailed—in the short-term, at least—by improved agricultural practices and crops, creative use of fossil fuels and energy efficiency, industrialization of the world, and development and widespread use of birth control.

We have exploited resources that other species formally used employing human intelligence, our phenomenal capacity to adapt culturally, our tendency to form groups, and our exceptional ability to work cooperatively. Humankind has benefited immensely, but not without altering the ecosphere significantly.

Reducing Our Numbers

Humans have been practicing birth control for millennia to curtail family size and to arrest population growth. People have used abstinence from sexual intercourse, sterilization, animal-intestine condoms, withdrawal before ejaculation, abortion, infanticide, and herbal medicines through recorded history. The understanding of ovulation, fertilization, and zygote implantation gained in the mid-20th century led the way for sophisticated contraception methods, ones that complemented time-tested, but less-effective, traditional means. Worldwide fertility programs led by the United Nations and governmental and not-for-profit organizations, coupled with economic development and education programs for women, led to a dramatic reduction in the average number of children per woman. World Bank data show that the global fertility rate decreased from 5 children per woman in 1960 to 2.5 in 2010, a decline of 50 percent. Over the same time period, global contraceptive use by women aged 15 to 49 increased from barely 5 percent to almost 65 percent, a rise of 1,300 percent. Clearly, major behavioral and social changes enabled by science—but not foreseen by Ehrlich in 1968—account for a much smaller global population today than Ehrlich and others envisioned.

That said, imagine what our population would be today had the vast majority of countries and people believed and acted upon the warnings of Malthus, Ehrlich, and others who understood exponential growth and knew that humanity was merely pushing into the future the Malthusian trap. We can never know, but perhaps contraceptive use would have approached 100 percent by the early 1990s, the fertility rate would have been below two children per woman, and we would have two billion fewer people than we currently do.

The major conclusion of the Commission on Population and the American Future, chaired by John D. Rockefeller III, was delivered in 1972: "We have looked for, and have not found, any convincing economic argument for continued population growth. The health of our country does not depend on it, nor does the vitality of business nor the welfare of the average person." To live well, we and Earth did not need more people then or now. It is important to appreciate that more people will not alleviate the mega environmental challenges facing societies across the globe, but rather, they would be easier to manage with fewer people. Knowing this can we adhere to the dictates of ecology and strive for both negative population and consumption growth?

CHAPTER 11

Economic System and Resources

H istory recounts humanity's varied solutions to the problem of providing for each person's needs in a way that facilitates group success. Until 300 years ago, the solutions that we employed for
organizing a society were not economic, as they are today. Rather, they fell
into two general categories: tradition and command. The *Endurance* Party
consisted of volunteers who employed mostly command with substantial
elements of tradition. Much like hunter-gatherers, Shackleton's men had no
need for a formal economic system because they either brought along or
foraged their resources.

Following the advent of agriculture some 10,000 years ago, more hierarchical arrangements better suited for larger sedentary communities replaced the patterns of resource allocation that sufficed for hunter-gatherers.
Trade that humans had long practiced became a major activity of settled
societies, as did markets for trading. The concept of money—objects representing some agreed-upon value—permitted transactions beyond simple barter.

Trade, money, and physical markets facilitated material transactions,
while globally connected communities emerged after the Dark Ages. The
discipline of economics, however, required a new idea, a creative way for
allocating resources and assuring a society's success. Robert Heilbroner, a
noted economist, writes:

[The necessity for economics] waited upon the development of an
astonishing arrangement in which society assured its own continuance by allowing each individual to do exactly as he saw fit—
provided he followed a central guiding rule. The arrangement was

called the "market system," and the rule was deceptively simple: each should do what was to his best monetary advantage. In the market system the lure of gain, not the pull of tradition or the whip of authority steered the great majority to his task.

This new arrangement emerged during the second half of the 18th century in England and Western Europe.

Adam Smith was an optimist and among the foremost philosophers and economic thinkers of his time—Thomas Malthus and David Ricardo were his colleagues. Smith is best known for the often-cited "invisible hand" in a short passage from his book *The Wealth of Nations*:

> Every individual ... neither intends to promote the public interest, nor knows how much he is promoting it. ... He intends only his own gain, and he is in this, as in many other cases, led by an invisible hand to promote an end which was no part of his intention. Nor is it always the worse for the society that it was no part of it. By pursuing his own interest he frequently promotes that of the society more effectually than when he really intends to promote it.

Today, most people who champion the "invisible hand" as the best way to serve the common good miss the explanation in Smith's companion book, *The Theory of Moral Sentiments*. Here Smith noted that the moral force of shared community values is required if a market economy driven by self-interest is to serve the public interest. In a city of millions, or a global economy of billions, the moral force of shared community values rarely, if ever, exists. The invisible hand works poorly today, if at all, because it lacks the context Smith gave.

Eighteenth and 19th-century economics focused on the interactions among three elements of production: land, labor, and capital. All were important, but especially land, because it grounded economic theory and practice in the natural world. Beginning early in the 20th century, neoclassical economists combined traditional capital—the equipment and structures used to produce goods and provide services—with land or natural capital: soil, forests, water, fisheries, stable climate, biodiversity and its life support functions. Thus, capital and labor became the two elements of production thereby allowing forms of capital to be freely exchangeable and priced by the market. For example, a parcel of forest land selling for $100,000 became equivalent to a tree cutting-processing machine of the same price. Persons could exchange one for the other with money. For an economist, a forest, fishery, hotel, and factory were capital stock available for production and services. Natural capital became commodities, things that we could manipulate and consume.

This kind of thinking created a worldview which economists strongly embraced for the better part of the past 100 years. With this perspective, the "economy" becomes the whole; the environment is merely one of its parts. The environment provides essentially unlimited possibilities for humans to make whatever they need. For example, if too little copper is available to make data-transmission wires, we invent a substitute, in this case fiber optics. Human creativity enables us to find a substitute whenever a resource becomes scarce. With the economy as the whole and the environment but one part, no limits on growth exist, even though Earth is finite. Simply put, Earth provides inputs to the economy that can grow forever. Is this a concocted arrangement within our economic system? Yes. Nevertheless, this is the assumption economists make to accommodate unlimited economic growth.

Capacity for unlimited physical growth is one of two major assumptions embraced by economists that conflicts with verifiable science. From space we see a finite Earth, not a human economy with potential for unlimited growth. In oceans, on land, and in the atmosphere, we observe with sophisticated instruments the influences that humans are having on the planet as well as the consequences of human activities on the forces that promote weather and climate. We understand feedback loops that make Antarctica the coldest place on Earth and know that melting glaciers there will, if unchecked, raise sea levels about 200 feet and radically alter climates. Also visible are vast areas of life that are part of the larger earth system, not the economy. The rules of the natural sciences apply to Earth and to the economy that functions within the ecosphere.

The second assumption emerged about100 years ago. Smith, Ricardo, Malthus, and other classical economists did not employ sophisticated mathematics to explain their economies. In 1881, Francis Edgeworth proposed in *Mathematical Psychics* that we could apply mathematics to economics by simplifying human behavior. He assumed that "every [hu]man is a pleasure machine" and that pleasure could be measured. Economists could then quantify economic behavior in addition to physical things. Using mathematics, economists sought the fundamental laws for economic behavior as physicists had done in their discipline. Economists wanted to treat their discipline as a predictive science. Over the years, economics gained stature, and the market economy became the organizing principle in industrial societies. Over this time, economists employed mathematically rigorous models to describe economic behavior; however, they did not validate their assumptions with how people behaved in society.

Physics is a predictive science because the objects of a particular type are all the same—electrons, neutrons, and protons, and the chemical elements they form. The behavior of a carbon atom is identical to that of all carbon atoms. It is the sameness of each object or actor and of their interactions that permit predictions of future outcomes with certainty in many situations. The uniformity of each particular actor and its interactions has permitted physicists to discern universal laws of behavior related to gravity, thermodynamics, electromagnetism, gases, diffusion, and others.

The fundamental objects or actors in economics, are individuals and groups of individuals—actors that never behave with the consistency of those in physics. As a result, we have found no universal fundamental laws of economic behavior. This reality is a consequence of the complexity of economic actors and the adaptive interactions among them. No two

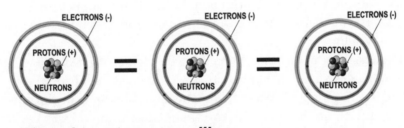

All carbon atoms are alike

No two people are alike

11.1: Fundamental actors in physics, for example, carbon atoms, are identical in behavior. In contrast, those in economics, for example people, are all unique in behavior.

humans behave identically, nor do any two groups, especially if they represent different cultures. Both reflect their respective societies and environments. Although economists appreciate this, they created a caricature called economic man. They have given this hypothetical-human universal traits: entirely self-centered, has insatiable wants satisfied by consumption, and is considered "rational" because he (she) always conforms to the caricature.

Economic models built on this hypothetical person supposedly predict individual and aggregate economic behaviors. Economic man behaves to maximize his happiness, or what economists call utility. Happiness is difficult to quantify, but money isn't, so economists equate happiness or utility with money. Economists know that more money beyond some base amount does not increase happiness. Humans in a group express cooperation, self-sacrifice, sensitivity, empathy, generosity, as well as selfishness, desires and wants, and consumption. At the same time, economists have not employed this set of behaviors in traditional economic models.

Individual and group economic behaviors are not very consistent, thereby making uniform laws of economic behavior and precise predictability unlikely. Only when economics squares the assumed behavior of its actors with their actual behavior might its pronouncements have consistent validity.

Interactions among the natural sciences, engineering, technology, and economics expanded the limits on growth that the land had previously imposed. Economics, however, did not completely eliminate the growth limits placed on biological systems. John Gowdy, an ecological economist, and Carl McDaniel summarize the relationship between economics and biology:

> The self-organizing principles of markets that have emerged in
> human cultures over the past 10,000 years are inherently in
> conflict with the self-organizing principles of ecosystems that have
> evolved over the past 3.5 billion years. The rules governing the
> dynamics of ecosystems, within which all human activity takes
> place, are ultimately a function of biological laws, not a function
> of human-created economic systems.

Over the past 100 years the small, central-Pacific island of Nauru tested the long-term capacity of our current economic system to promote human well-being and preserve life support functions. The Nauruans had a culture perhaps 3,000 years old that had served them well. They had minimal contact with the rest of humanity resulting in a culture and language whose origins are obscure.

Western influences arrived early in the 19th century followed by discovery in 1900 of one of the world's richest deposits of phosphate ore—the entire island was composed of coral skeletal remains and phosphate ore. In the mid-1980s, Nauruans were among the richest, if not the richest, people per capita in the world. Sadly, today the island is a wasteland of coral pinnacles. Its inhabitants are dependent on imports. Without resupply, Nauru's population of 10,000 could fall below the 1,200 inhabitants who welcomed westerners 200 years ago.

The carrying capacity of our planet was likely passed half a century ago when our number was closer to 3 billion. This estimated carrying capacity is, of course, dependent upon the state of earth systems, technologies employed, and consumption. However, the current scale of human activities increases average temperatures, modifies and intensifies weather patterns, alters fire cycles, degrades soil fertility, pollutes water supplies and soils, and extirpates species. We have continued to grow our economy by consuming life-support capital—stocks of fish and trees, fertile soil, water in rivers and aquifers, and space—and by overwhelming Earth's capacity to assimilate wastes. These wastes include heat-trapping gases in the atmosphere, chemicals from industrial agriculture in soil and water, heavy metals, persistent organic chemicals, radioactive compounds, and innumerable human-created toxic and ecosystem-disrupting substances in soil, water, and air. This degradation of Earth's capacity to support life and assimilate waste will constrain humanity's choices to provide for its increasing numbers. Options may be as constrained as they were for Shackleton and his men, perhaps more so.

Side Note 12.
- The history of human habitation is replete with societies that overexploited resources and experienced a local collapse in quality-of-life and of population.
- The trajectory of impoverishing biodiversity and the life support it provides foretells collapses on a global scale.

Creating a Reality-Based Economic System and Use of Resources

As far back as the mid-19th century, John Stuart Mill, noted English philosopher and economist, posited that the economy will achieve a steady-state in which population and human activities will maintain a dynamic equilibrium with the rest of nature while improvements in technology and the widening of ethical considerations will continue. In the second half of the 20th century, Herman Daly, the father of ecological economics, also believed that we could resolve the fundamental conflicts with biophysical reality outlined above. How? By creating the type of economy Mill envisioned that never materialized. In contrast, Daly recognized that abandoning the quest for never ending economic growth would be difficult for economists, because to do so would render economics textbooks and much of economic policy obsolete. Additionally, shifting to a new economic model has many difficulties. At the same time, Daly appreciated that parts of microeconomics and market theory in particular would be useful in establishing a steady-state economy, a dynamic state of persistent innovation and change without perpetual physical growth.

What would a steady-state economy look like? To start, it would have to achieve two major goals: 1) a population sized for compatibility with the necessary resources to maintain a desired quality of life and 2) material and energy flow (throughput) compatible with Earth's capacity to provide this level of resource flow on an ongoing basis. We would then need public policies and actions that would permit us to maintain and adjust this dynamic equilibrium between population and resources as circumstances dictate.

Daly suggested in 1990 three important rules for a steady-state economy:

1. Exploit renewable resources no faster than they can be regenerated.
2. Deplete nonrenewable resources no faster than the rate at which renewable substitutes can be developed.
3. Emit wastes no faster than they can be safely assimilated by ecosystems.

We are currently failing on all three counts.

Attaining a steady-state economy will require a radical departure from business as usual. At the same time, shifting to such an economy will bring many positive outcomes. Things that can improve or increase in quality, number or diversity—wisdom, ethics, products, knowledge, community relations, forms and characteristics of social institutions and businesses, entertainment, breadth and depth of learning, and measurements that actually quantify the quality of life—all of which can enhance the quality of life. At the same time, only little needs to hold steady: human population size, the stock of human-built capital, and throughput. What is perhaps surprising to some of us is that human societies have been attempting to bring about many of these changes for a long time. That is, we already have a good idea of how to accomplish this transition.

Success stories about reducing fertility rates abound, one of which I discussed earlier—providing women with the knowledge and means to choose the number of children they want. Educating women and allowing them to participate in the economy reduces birth rates significantly. These and other approaches, coupled with a society's decision to achieve a population size compatible with its resources, can lead to a durable population size—likely lower than currently exists—within several generations.

The annual throughput that the average person in the United States uses is a quantity most people understand. However, what a country and the world consume overwhelms one's mind. Before I give a few numbers, let us try to fathom just how big some of these numbers are. If you begin clapping your hands at a rate of one clap per second, how long will it take to clap 60 times? OK, one minute. To clap 3,600 times? Right, one hour. How many claps per day? Yes, 86,400. That's quite a few claps but a number that we can grasp. Now, how long for a million claps? A billion claps? A trillion claps? The answers are 12 days, 32 years, and 32,000 years. If all you did was clap, you would be able to clap between 2 and 3 billion times in your lifetime! Millions, billions, and trillions are big numbers that are difficult to understand. Often our minds glaze over, and we go on. Nevertheless, it is imperative that we appreciate and act on the consequences of these big numbers, if humanity is to have a bright future.

In 2007 the average individual in the United States consumed annually 270 pounds of meat. How much did we consume as a country? 81 billion pounds. The world average was 103 pounds per person. The world total was 721 billion pounds. In 2011 the average person in the United States consumed 77 pounds of sugar, or 23 billion pounds nationally. On the energy side, each person in the United States used 446 gallons of gasoline, or 134 billion gallons nationally. In 2011 the United States used 97 quadrillion (97,000,000,000,000,000) British thermal units (BTUs) which averages to 320 million BTUs per person. The world in 2009 used 483 quadrillion

BTUs. These are big numbers! It is their remorseless consequences on resources, the climate, and biodiversity that threaten prosperity. As we have discussed earlier, humanity is taking for itself much of Earth's life support capacity, leaving less for the rest of nature and its descendants.

Many people want to believe that growing the economy and preserving the environment are compatible. They talk about increasing the number of green jobs, shifting to renewable energy by installing more photovoltaic panels and wind turbines, and driving electric cars and trucks charged with solar electricity to show that compatibility is possible. Unfortunately, these are microeconomic considerations and do not deal with the big numbers considered above in the aggregate—the macroeconomy. Look out the window of a low flying airplane to see the macroeconomy: houses, factories, highways, parking lots, airports, military installations, telephone poles, trucks, cars, trains, warehouses and all manner of other commercial buildings, parks and recreational areas, bicycles, baby carriages, and all the rest. The growth in global production and consumption of goods and services of this macroeconomy in the aggregate is in conflict with environmental preservation. We have a "full world," as Daly says, where economic growth is at the expense of life support capacity. The result—climate change, sixth mass extinction, human population and consumption beyond Earth's carrying capacity.

A major obstacle to a durable economy is the delusion that economic growth has no limit. In this regard the stories that we tell ourselves within a society are the stories we believe. The ones we deeply believe become the stories upon which we act. In this way we create our future. It is past time to deeply believe the stories science tells and act on them to create an enduring future.

CHAPTER 12

Leadership and Durable Societies

The Weddell Sea Party included diverse human personalities. Under Shackleton's leadership the men managed to function effectively despite extreme physical and emotional stress. At the outset they were simply individuals, not the invincible team they would become. When the *Endurance* sailed from London on August 1, 1914, Shackleton and Wild were not aboard. They remained behind to finalize finances and tie up loose ends while Worsley sailed the ship to Buenos Aires.

The Skipper's strength was not leadership. He indulged his moods and could not instill discipline or curtail conflict. This was evident during the two-month sail to Argentina when many of the professionals aboard grew homesick and questioned why they'd joined in the first place. Some of the seamen became unruly, a behavior that continued in Buenos Aires, where some of the crew did nothing but party, often all night. Shackleton arrived on October 26 to encounter a team plagued by conflict, cliques, little productivity, and no useful routine.

Learning of these problems, Boss stayed at a hotel for several days to assess the situation instead of going onboard immediately. He fired the ship's incompetent cook and hired Green, who would prove invaluable. He dismissed three seamen and hired Bakewell. With his typical grace, Shackleton helped the fired seamen find jobs on a ship bound for England. Finally, when red tape was preventing the *Endurance* from departing, he charmed Argentine officials to gain the necessary permits.

Once aboard the *Endurance,* Shackleton shared his cabin with Worsley for the first few months so they could get to know each other. In like manner, he regularly interacted one-on-one with every man. In this way he gained an in-depth understanding of his men that enabled him to learn their strengths and weaknesses and to create mutual respect and trust.

As a child, Shackleton loved to read—about anything. Early in his career at sea, a colleague offered this description of Shackleton's cabin: "On one side a writing table, with the wall behind covered with photos of friends, and on the other wall a bookcase with signs of a well-read owner, for in it I saw Shakespeare, Longfellow, Darwin, and Dickens, as well as books on navigation." Shackleton read the Bible, was inspired by poetry—especially that of Alfred Lord Tennyson and Robert Browning—and found "the history of people struggling to be free, of adventurous nations who sent their mariners into unknown seas, and the history of colonization and exploration" especially engaging. His book knowledge, blended with his merchant marine travels to Africa, China, Europe, the Far East, the Middle East, South America, and the United States, enabled Shackleton to speak intelligently on almost any subject. He used this invaluable asset when interacting with his men, raising money from the elite, and passing months adrift in the Weddell Sea.

Because he knew the talents, skills, behaviors, and characters of his men well, Shackelton avoided problems and effectively assigned men and promoted daily activities. For example, he considered Hudson, Hurley, James, and McNeish potential troublemakers, so he assigned them to his or Wild's tent where they would be less likely to influence or annoy others. For the three boats, he put together crews that were balanced in terms of skills and personalities. Additionally, he selected the men to sail the *Caird* to South Georgia for their talents and critical skills (Crean, McCarthy, McNeish, and Worsley) and their potential as problem-makers for Wild back on land (Crean, McNeish, Vincent).

Boss spoke softly and slowly. His engagement was always purposeful. He was exceptionally talented at organizing—food, equipment, tools, technical instruments, clothes, logistics. Goal-oriented, he never lost sight of the ultimate objective while effectively tending to the day's tasks. He made decisions only after pondering every option, often for days or longer. When one plan or course of action failed, he learned from it and moved on, never dwelling on the past or assigning blame. When the crew abandoned the *Endurance*, his words to the men were simple: "So now we'll go home." About the loss of the *Endurance*, he wrote, "A man must shape himself to a new mark directly [when] the old one goes to ground."

Upon realizing that the ship would be lost to the ice, Shackleton confided only in Wild and Worsley. Several times while on the floes and in the boats, he kept bad news to himself. Never did he or the other leaders reveal their doubts about surviving, nor did the crew to any extent. It was taboo. Of course, it was clear to all that they were in a terrible predicament. Boss, as anyone, liked and got along with some of his men better than others, but he masked his feelings well. Deciding when to reveal the truth or openly discuss a dire situation was relatively easy for him because he knew his men and the situation well—today's leaders face in many instances a far more difficult challenge with huge, diverse audiences and complex situations.

Shackleton set a tone and standards for daily life. He established a routine for meals, ship's work, and discretionary time—a routine that defined expectations for the men and injected order, purpose, and discipline into their lives. Almost everything he did fostered unity and cooperation. Simply put, his past experiences—especially his Antarctic expeditions—had forged in him the absolute belief that if he could elicit each man's best effort, including a desire to go the extra mile for the group, he would have a united, loyal team that could succeed at any challenge. He achieved this outcome through a host of interdependent approaches.

Although each man brought a special talent or skill to the group, everyone participated in ship's work, assisted in scientific experiments and data collection, and familiarized themselves with all aspects of the expedition. The seaman learned from scientists, while the scientists and other professionals gained knowledge about sailing the ship. All—even Shackleton—stood watches, scrubbed decks, maintained boiler fires, had time at the helm steering, shoveled coal, moved and stowed food and other provisions, and cared for the dogs.

Wild, although different in personality from Shackleton, learned so well from Boss—beginning with their first journey together during Scott's initial attempt at the South Pole—that he slipped perfectly into Shackleton's shoes when left in charge on Elephant Island. Wild was the ideal executive officer. We cannot say enough about his leadership, which maintained *esprit de corps* and the health of 22 men for 4 months on a desolate, godforsaken beach at the end of the world.

Working together, the men came to value each other's contributions to both routine tasks and to the overall expedition. As the group's knowledge broadened, each man came to know enough to be helpful on most tasks. Equally important, they came to know each other in an egalitarian atmosphere of cooperation and trust.

Shackleton's apprenticeship in the British Merchant Marine Service amounted to four unhappy years at sea aboard three clipper ships that hauled cargo around the world. While that crucible taught him that life at sea was hard and often brutal, he realized that a sailor's life need not be miserable. Six years later, as the third mate on the *Tintagel Castle* that was carrying troops to the Boer War in South Africa, Shackleton used entertainment—concerts, sports, a festival of crossing the equator—to enliven the demoralized crew. He became "the life and soul" of the ship, according to one crewman. By the time *Endurance* sailed for Antarctica, Shackleton was a master at reading a crew's morale, and he knew when to hold a special event. After the *Endurance* sank, Shackleton had Green serve special treats for dinner of fish paste and biscuits. He also encouraged and actively participated in regular entertainment—plays in the Ritz, soccer, dog races, singing, game playing—and was always good for a laugh or practical joke.

Shackleton's leadership style reduced significantly the distinctions among the officers, professionals (scientists and artisans), and seaman, but hierarchical relationships remained and were necessary. Shackleton, Wild, Worsley, and Greenstreet had command, and the crew followed directions. McNeish's overt rejection of a direct order from Worsley and then Shackleton was a notable exception. At the same time, Shackleton accommodated personality differences as long as they didn't negatively affect others. For example, he tolerated Orde-Lees shirking his fair share and James's lack of technical skills and his tendency not to join in. He acknowledged Hurley's need to feel important and to have confidence in proposals, and accepted Green's idiosyncrasies. However, he did not tolerate Vincent's bullying of his fellow seamen and firemen.

Humans, individually and as a group, react negatively when a person or group is treated unfairly. The standard response is to punish the perpetrator(s). Shackleton knew this well, as illustrated by his method of food distribution in each tent:

> [E]verything is most carefully and accurately divided into as many equal portions as there are men in that tent. One member then closes his eyes or turns his head away and calls out the names at random, as the cook for the day points to each portion, saying at the same time, "Whose?"
>
> Partiality, however unintentional it may be, is thus entirely obviated and everyone feels satisfied that all is fair, even though one may look a little enviously at the next man's helping.

Equity and fairness were hallmarks of Shackleton's leadership. In fact, not only did he expect others to treat him no differently than anyone else, but he also elected to inflict on himself an unfair, or at least an unequal, deal. In 1908, during Shackleton's forced return after failing to reach the South Pole, bad weather, dysentery, and a lack of food plagued his four-man team. At one desperate time, Shackleton forced Wild to take his only breakfast biscuit.

After abandoning *Endurance*, the men spent a miserable first night on the floes. Dead tired, they slept directly on snow, or on a board or piece of cloth, wrapping themselves around one another for warmth. Shackleton himself stood watch that night.

Once on the ice, the men needed sleeping bags. They hadn't planned to lose the ship and had just 18 fur bags for 28 men. Ten men would have to make do with inferior Jaeger woolen bags and a reindeer skin. To be fair, the fur bags would be distributed by lottery. Shackleton, Wild, Worsley, and a few other old hands elected not to participate. They chose the woolen bags.

Shackleton was an astute student of human behavior who exquisitely applied his knowledge not only in selecting men for the expedition but also in shaping them into an unassailable force. Those who served with him, especially on the *Endurance*, recognized his genius. Many others over time have seen this genius and rank the story of the *Endurance* Party as the most notable survival adventure in recorded history.

Academics, heads of major corporations, military leaders, and leadership consultants, among others, have written about and used the survival of the *Endurance* Party to illustrate and teach leadership. Dennis Perkins, in *Leading at the Edge: Leadership Lessons from the Extraordinary Saga of Shackleton's Antarctic Expedition*, tells why:

> In my search to find compelling examples of what can be accomplished when people work together to overcome adversity…the story of the *Endurance* was unique. Better than any other, the Shackleton saga encapsulated the strategies I had found to be absolutely essential for success…and for illustrating the key ideas about extraordinary leadership and teamwork.

The challenge of enabling billions of people in diverse societies to cooperate and sufficiently discipline themselves to resolve the major environmental issues that threaten us dwarfs the task of creating a group of 28 men that expressed the cooperation and discipline required to function effectively in dire straits. Yet, this is required if a globalized world and its numerous societies are to avoid coming undone.

We cannot scale some of the strategies that Shackleton employed to create his invincible team to groups of thousands or millions of individuals—a leader getting to know every subordinate well, each person learning about and participating in all aspects of an organization, and every person knowing everyone else well enough for all around mutual trust and respect. However, we can employ much of Shackleton's brilliant use of human nature with large groups.

The natural sciences and biology in particular have discovered much about human nature—how genes and certain epigenetic phenomena influence behavior and shape personality. In the 1930s, a grand synthesis of cell biology, development, genetics, morphology, and physiology occurred to authenticate Darwinian evolution as the uniting idea in biology. However, another 4 decades would pass before the genetic basis of human behavior began to truly yield to scientific inquiry. In 1975 Wilson summarized in *Sociobiology* the evidence for behavioral genetics in social organisms, concluding with a chapter on human behavior. All hell broke loose! Many people, including some of Wilson's colleagues, firmly believed human behavior was exclusively molded by the environment. They rebuked him in their writings and in public pronouncements. At the national meeting of the American Association for the Advancement of Science in 1978 a person walked onto the platform where Wilson sat waiting to speak. He proceeded to pour a pitcher of water on Wilson while he and colleagues chanted, "Wilson you're all wet!" Within a decade or two, the dust had settled. Wilson had it right—genes and the rules for their expression are the foundations of human behavior.

Social behavior in apes and monkeys dates back some 40 million years. With every split of their branch of the evolutionary tree—first, the separation of old world versus new world monkeys, then apes and old world monkeys, and more recently chimpanzees and humans—each species took a different path. The type of habitat entered helps shape a species social behavior. For *Homo sapiens* and its two closest living relatives, *Pans paniscus* (bonobo) and *Pans troglodytes* (chimpanzee), each has a nature composed of unique as well as shared behavioral traits that together create their particular sociality. All three make political alliances, but chimpanzees and humans express more violence than bonobos. The social glue for bonobos is overt sexual interactions while these relations in humans are less common and more secretive and selective. All of this is to say that each social animal—from prairie dog to termite—has a unique nature adaptive to its circumstances.

We can state simply the message from the survival of Shackleton's *Endurance* Party as it relates to 21st century humanity. For humankind to create durable societies, its institutions must promote civil relations of trust, respect, equity and fairness as well as apply the rules and enlightenment that evidence-based disciplines provide when making important decisions. It will be essential to employ all we know, and continue to learn, about human nature. The civil society that Shackleton and his men made, as well as the leadership model he employed, were crucial to their survival and may well provide critical insights for fashioning enduring societies.

Creating Durable Societies

The *Endurance* Party had five characteristics that favored its transformation to a team capable of survival. First was its size. Human behavior was honed to its current form over the span of hundreds of thousands of years, if not millions, when humans lived in bands composed of a few dozen hunter-gatherers, first in Africa and then beyond. We've evolved to work well and survive in small groups the size of the Weddell Sea Party, often under similarly adverse conditions.

Second, the adventurers were a handpicked group of men bolstered with a core of hardened disciplined sailors and explorers who accepted a command-and-tradition-based organization. Third, Shackleton selected each man for specific talents and expertise for the expedition and that complemented those of others. Fourth, Shackleton and Wild exhibited exceptionally complementary leadership skills. Lastly, the men accepted evidence-based, verifiable reality and acted accordingly.

Notwithstanding these advantages, which modern humankind as a whole does not share, we can glean relevant aspects from the *Endurance* story that may be useful in creating durable societies. While the *Endurance* Party's economy was barter—certainly an unworkable arrangement for billions of people—the pay scale they used remains relevant today. The ratio of highest-to-lowest paid was 3:1 ($750 [scientists]: $240 [seamen]). The ratio of highest-to-lowest paid worker in the United States today is 3,900:1 ($57,000,000 [12 highest paid CEOs ranged from $41 million to $131 million]:$14,500 [minimum wage of $7.25; 8-hour-day for 50 weeks]). No one's compensation is thousands of times greater than another's except in an economic arrangement that is heavily tilted to favor particular people regardless of their actual value to the group's wellbeing.

A recent analysis indicates that rich societies that deliver the highest quality of life to their citizens—education, health care, safety, social mobility, trust, community life, child well-being, and low levels of obesity and imprisonment—are also the most equitable. The study compared 23 of the world's richest countries, and each of the states in the United States. Those with the best quality of life and narrowest wealth distribution were Japan, the Scandinavian countries, and the state of New Hampshire. The rest of the states, the United States itself, and the United Kingdom delivered the lowest quality of life and exhibited the widest wealth distribution. Consistent with this assessment is the ratio of average CEO to average worker pay in Japan and the United States, 11:1 and 475:1, respectively.

The Weddell Sea Party practiced fairness in all matters. Distributions of food, clothing, accommodations, bedding, and the work expected were not always equal, but the way they were allocated was fair and forthright. This pervasive fairness bonded the men together, permitting the social cohesiveness required in challenging situations and enabling the group to share its conviction that things would improve. Just how this cohesiveness and unity are evoked in a world of billions of people is far from clear; however, culturally reinforced standards of fairness and equity are requisite. Societies without them will likely struggle to remain intact in the hard times ahead.

Shackleton's public face never wavered—they were going to beat the odds—and his demand for a collective optimism paid off: the men were able to endure repeated exertions beyond exhaustion and long periods of absolute boredom. Interestingly, Shackleton's unfailing belief in himself and in success—as well as the other's unwavering faith in him—demonstrate the capacity of humans to believe anything, despite the hopelessness of a situation. We might put to advantage this facet of human nature in creating durable societies.

Behind his back, his men who knew Shackleton's careful, thoughtful, risk-averse behavior and decision making well called him "Cautious Jack". Shackleton forbade Orde-Lees from riding his bicycle alone and admonished others for foolish behavior that might have jeopardized safety. Shackleton resisted taking to the boats until their floe broke apart. Yet, when they landed on Elephant Island with no chance of rescue, he took the risk of leaving 22 men behind while attempting to sail a 22½-foot lifeboat through the world's most treacherous seas. He then trekked across the *terra incognito* of South Georgia. Risk aversion is often the best policy; but in dire straits, big risks may be the only option.

Over time, it became apparent to every man in the group that they were incapable of affecting their own fate apart from responding well to what came. This realization might have demoralized them but Shackleton's goal oriented leadership gave purpose to their lives. He had built his team with the objective of crossing Antarctica that then shifted to survival and getting home. Perhaps the greatest obstacle humankind faces today is first accepting that mega-environmental crises are here and then acting purposefully to resolve them.

Human groups have a strong propensity for hierarchy and for establishing rules that enforce such rankings. Behaviors that evolved during our long history as hunter-gatherers created groups that were more egalitarian than almost all others since the adoption of agriculture some 10,000 years ago. This history affirms that human nature is compatible with rule-based social arrangements that are fundamentally egalitarian. The mandate is to adopt rules and policies that foster equitable, vibrant societies that enable their members to care well for one another while dampening disparities in wealth and opportunity.

Shackleton was a great leader who had no place in his leadership style for rank-has-its-privileges (RHIP). How many of our business, political, religious, sports and entertainment leaders shun RHIP and employ Shackleton-like leadership? Among billions of people we certainly have innumerable Shackletons and potential Shackletons. Our task is to create social relations and conditions that nurture, bring forth, and affirm Shackleton type leaders who shun personal reward and aggrandizement, champion equitable treatment, and consider a leadership position reward enough. We have always needed leaders with these qualities but there have been too few. Humans have squeaked by because resources abounded; however, scarcities are becoming the norm—the free board on our craft is vanishing. Without many more exceptional leaders our floundering boat will likely founder.

The success of the natural sciences and other evidence-based disciplines in demystifying much that our ancestors explained with concocted alternative realities proves that humans are capable of using rational thought. This gave humankind an authentic and believable creation story. The charge now is to create societies that bring scientifically verifiable evidence and rational thought to bear on important decisions. It may then be possible for societies across the globe to realize in the present the heretofore distant vision of wholesome, durable, equitable patterns of habitation.

Coda

I had an unanticipated reaction to the news in May 2013 that the concentration of CO_2 in the atmosphere had passed an unfortunate milestone by reaching a level of 400 ppm. For more than two decades, I worried about the ever-increasing CO_2 level, but, for some reason—I'm not sure why—reaching 400 evoked a calm acceptance of what I had long known. Perhaps my optimistic side had encouraged me to believe that as long as the concentration remained in the 300s, slowing of the increase followed by a downturn was possible. Nevertheless, reaching 400 ppm, with the rate still accelerating, confirms that we can expect major climate change. The task now is to lessen its severity by reducing as fast as possible the release of heat trapping gases and be prepared to adjust to what comes.

Unfortunately, reaching the 400 mark caused little reaction within the general public. In October 1999, when our population reached 6 billion and made global news, few people took seriously its implications. Fourteen years later, no nation has given top priority to addressing over population or excessive consumption, and we've added more than a billion people. Preserving biodiversity and realigning the global political market economy to match natural limits on growth remain minor concerns when they register at all. People across the globe still believe that business as usual will deliver the best of futures. However, we cannot haul the status quo to *terra firma*—it is biophysically impossible.

The natural sciences and other evidence-based disciplines have not only indicated that the human enterprise is on a collision course with biological reality, but have also provided proof that our actions are undoing the capacity of Earth to support us. In this lies the fundamental paradox of our time: the ramifications of our successes are underwriting our demise. Resolving this paradox—reconfiguring human activities so as to promote human wellbeing while achieving a durable future—is the intractable problem we have created but must now resolve to avoid unpleasant consequences.

The natural sciences have bound themselves together with evidence-based, verifiable understandings through the unity of knowledge. Each discipline complies with the rules of the more fundamental underlying discipline(s). The natural sciences have thus provided a possible way to resolve our paradox. If the social sciences and humanities emulate the unity of knowledge achieved in the natural sciences, together we might affect the resolution.

The framework for the aesthetic, intellectual, and practical doings of the social sciences and humanities over the past several hundred years was anchored on two assumptions:

- Earth was the center not only of our solar system but also the universe.
- Humans were divinely created as the crown jewel of the earthly biological world.

Both were disproved. Nicoholas Copernicus in 1543 debunked the first assumption in *On the Revolutions of the Heavenly Spheres*. Darwin the second in 1859 with *The Origin of Species*.

Unfortunately, humans accept radical change to a worldview first not at all, then at a glacially slow pace. It took centuries for the general acceptance of Earth's true rank as a small planet rotating around a minor star in a galaxy far from the center of the universe. Most of humanity has yet to accept the Darwinian explanation.

Intellectual accomplishments (and any endeavor) based on false assumptions can lead to verbose unintelligible gibberish and unintended outcomes. Biologists in the early 20th century, for example, assumed that proteins must be the genetic material because of their complexity. The models based on this assumption were convoluted. The code for genetic information unreachable. Science had to scrap all that work when in 1944 researchers found that DNA played this role. Similarly, many findings in the humanities and social sciences that depended upon the two false assumptions above require updating.

The Standard Social Science Model, articulated in the early 20th century, has been the accepted framework employed by academics over much of the past century for studying and understanding social and cultural phenomena. The model assumed that the social sciences were their own domain and had only to be internally consistent. By excluding the methods and results of the natural sciences, especially biology, progress in explaining and understanding social and cultural phenomena was severely hampered.

For example, following the rediscovery of Mendelian genetics in 1900, it became clear in a few decades that the phenotype of an organism (e.g., eye color, wing shape, size, when a plant flowers, and then the behavior of animals) was not only influenced by its environment, but also by its genotype. That is, the particular alleles of the genes which an organism carries. For example, a red eye and a white eye allele in the fruit fly are two possible variants of the gene that determines eye color. In effect, interplay between nature (its genotype) and nurture (its environment) determine an individual's phenotype. The 2002 publication of *The Blank Slate: The Modern Denial of Human Nature* by Steven Pinker, a psychologist of visual cognition and language, pointed out that many people still held the long-standing misconception that environment alone shapes human behavior.

The belief that either nature or nurture alone determines phenotype far exceeds an academic discussion. It had and does have real-world consequences. In the late 1920s, Russian agricultural technician Trofim Lysenko purported that he had changed biennial wheat into annual wheat by environmental manipulations and that he could similarly change the phenotype of any plant. Lysenko's poorly conducted experiments and fabricated results fit well with the ideology of the Soviet Union at the time—that people's behavior is exclusively a product of their environment.

Those with power and influence in the Soviet Union embraced Lysenko and his ideas, thereby giving them status and power. The regime purged geneticists and sent world-renowned scientists like botanist Nikolai Vavilov, who had worked out the origins of many of the world's food plants, to prison. In 1948, Joseph Stalin outlawed genetics as "bourgeois science" and "alien to the principles of socialism." It wasn't until the mid 1960s that the Soviet Union permitted the study of genetics. Millions of people died mostly from starvation because the agricultural establishment banned plant breeding and other sound practices in favor of pseudoscience. Nazi Germany adopted the other equally wrong extreme—nature determined a person's behavior. The results were again devastating for large numbers of people. These regrettable outcomes and other missteps justify questioning assumptions in all endeavors.

In the practice of the natural sciences, the veracity of a conclusion rests on the validity of the underlying assumptions that are stated in the context of the work. False assumptions and other discrepancies are eventually discovered because science is a self-correcting process. The holy grail of science is discovery of a major error or of something unknown, but important. As a result, scientists put intense efforts at the frontiers of their disciplines for new discoveries and corrections of significance.

In the past few decades the Standard Social Science Model has fallen out of favor. Emerging in its place is an integrated model that seeks to build upon the natural sciences, biology in particular. This change is needed. Until political science and our culture deliver politicians who universally employ evidence-based decision making, we shall experience Lysenko-type missteps (e.g., climate instability, extinction of species and ecosystems, over population and excessive consumption, perpetuation of a dysfunctional economic system). Only when economics scraps its growth-now-and-forever mantra thereby accepting the realities of our planet's resources and formulates models based on how humans actually behave, can we begin in earnest to create a durable, steady-state economy that functions within the constraints of biology and physics.

Spirituality emerged in our hunter-gatherer ancestors to become a powerful element of human nature. Ever since then, spirits, mystical powers, and gods have held sway over our communal and individual behaviors. Today practiced religions number between 800 and 4,000, depending on the criteria one applies. The ubiquity of religions, now and in the past, and their capacity to bind a group of people together with common purpose and ethics indicate that the faith instinct likely played a major role not only in a group's success but also in humanity's survival.

As modern science began providing increasingly more authentic explanations of spirits, mystical powers, and even the gods of old, it became clear that the faith instinct was here to stay—it was in our genes. Humanity has come to embrace two fundamentally opposing worldviews: one transcendental, the other empirical. The first worldview was a product of the brain in its attempt to make sense of the world. The second by the brain's naturally selected intellectual, logical, and analytical powers. Human inventions extended the capacity of these powers to open the previously invisible world of innumerable things, including the electromagnetic spectrum, gravity, plate tectonics, atoms, hormones, and evolution.

A 22-year-old Charles Darwin embarked on a 5-year circumnavigation of the globe on the *H.M.S Beagle* as a devout Christian. Had he not attained his position on the *Beagle*, he would likely have become a pastor. As the expedition's scientist, he kept a meticulous journal on the natural history and geology he witnessed. Darwin was a keen observer with an exceptional intellect and much curiosity.

He knew of the idea of evolution before the voyage—Erasmus Darwin, his grandfather, espoused evolution in his poetry and conversation. The young

Darwin was open to the idea as a consequence. The flora and fauna, as well as the fossils he observed and carefully described increasingly caused him to question the accepted belief that species were fixed in form by God their creator. Mounting evidence indicated otherwise, but by what mechanism?

During the several years after his voyage, Darwin formulated arguably the most powerful and liberating idea in history—evolution by natural selection. Over the next two decades, he honed the concept and supporting evidence until he was compelled in 1859 to publish *On the Origin of Species*. In 1858, Darwin and Alfred Russell Wallace, the co-discoverer of evolution by natural selection, had each presented a paper on evolution at the London meeting of the Linnaean Society. Wallace had forced Darwin's hand.

Wilson encapsulates well what the voyage on the *Beagle* brought about in Darwin's mind and the meaning of that transformation for humanity:

> The great naturalist did not abandon Abrahamic and other religious dogmas because of his discovery of evolution by natural selection, as one might reasonably suppose. The reverse occurred. The shedding of blind faith gave him the intellectual fearlessness to explore human evolution wherever logic and evidence took him. And so he set forth boldly, in *The Descent of Man* to track the origin of humanity, and in *The Expression of the Emotions in Man and Animals* to address the evolution of instinct. Thus was born scientific humanism, the only worldview compatible with science's growing knowledge of the real world and the laws of nature.

As flawed as creation myths are in light of today's knowledge, they were the beginning of a people's forthright attempt to explain their surroundings and the human place in them. Science has carried on this tradition to establish humankind's evidence-based, verifiable creation story, one that some Christians and other religious individuals have embraced. Michael Dowd, an ordained minister and author of *Thank God for Evolution*, writes: "Ecology is the new theology. Big history is the new Genesis. Those who fail to understand that evidence is modern-day Scripture, and that the world we live in is an honorable world, betray God and humanity in the most egregious of ways."

Thomas Berry, a Roman Catholic priest and historian of cultures, writes in *Dream of the Earth*:

[T]he existing religious traditions are too distant from our new sense of the universe to be adequate to the task that is before us. We cannot do without the traditional religions, but they cannot presently do what needs to be done. We need a new type of religious orientation. This must, in my view, emerge from our new story of the universe.

In *The Great Work* Berry presents what needs to emerge from our creation story:

The Great Work now, as we move into a new millennium, is to carry out the transition from a period of human devastation of the Earth to a period when humans would be present to the planet in a mutually beneficial manner. ... Such a transition has no historical parallel since the geobiological transition that took place 67 million years ago when the period of the dinosaurs was terminated and a new biological age begun. So now we awaken to a period of extensive disarray in the biological structure and functioning of the planet.

Humans were not around at the time of the last transition—biological evolution handled the birthing of a new age and the rise of human dominion. If human-driven geophysical and biological changes continue on their current trajectories, humanity, or at least civilization, will likely be the victim, as the dinosaurs were so long ago. If, however, we are able to escape the trap we set for ourselves, religion will likely play a pivotal role in freeing us as it did in setting the trap in the first place.

Religion has been and will continue, of course, to be a doubled-edged sword—the good and the bad. It unites a group in its conflicts with other groups, provides ethical standards of behavior, gives people purpose and meaning, promotes altruistic actions, offers assistance and comfort to the sick and distressed, and establishes rites of passage during life and in death. Over time, religion fostered the most admirable of culture's accomplishments: among the best of the arts and music, rituals that united people in a purposeful existence, and the atmosphere in which altruistic behavior thrived—empathy, concern, and help for others.

Religion's bad edge has been sharpened too. A hunter-gatherer group obedient to its god's pronouncements that engendered cooperation was better than less-cohesive groups at doing what they needed for survival. The enhanced reproductive success—bottom line of natural selection—often involved competition among groups for resources (e.g., food, territory, women). As rules attributed to higher powers became pervasive and influential in human groups, competitive interactions that had been violent became even more so. Nicholas Wade, scientific writer and journalist, writes in *The Faith Instinct*:

> [A] typical tribal society lost about 0.5 percent of its population in combat each year, far more than the toll suffered by most modern states—war deaths in the twentieth century would have amounted to 2 billion people had the tribal death rate persisted.
>
> Pre-state societies fought often. About 75 percent went to war at least every two years, until they were pacified, whereas the modern nation state goes to war about once a generation. Adding to the carnage, primitive peoples were not in the habit of taking prisoners … captured warriors were killed on the spot.

The ethical rules and behaviors brought forth by religion have been, by and large, for the benefit of the group and its members. Outsiders or others were treated differently. For some hunter-gatherers, the first thought when meeting a stranger was, "Why should I not kill him?" In the name of religion, outsiders and nonbelievers have been tortured, lost fingers and hands, imprisoned, forced into slavery, starved, or just killed. Religion was apparently a major evolutionary force leading to the pervasive worldview of "us" versus "them"—being an outsider was an unhealthy status. Radical religious groups of all stripes have exacerbated even more this long standing negative attribute of religion that at its origin was adaptive for hunter-gatherer groups.

Over the long sweep of time, religion has nurtured humanity's angels and demons. Can we transform religion in its multiplicity of forms to favor the "good" and diminish significantly the "bad"? In the arenas where it truly matters, can a new evidence-based scripture become the norm? Can we preserve the basic positive tenants of the major religions of the world, which are essentially the same, and still root out evil? That is, can religion metamorphose into a more inclusive and authentic system of beliefs that gives meaning and purpose to life?

I do not know the answers to these questions, nor does anyone. At the same time, it is reasonable to argue that radical changes will take too long knowing that 1) it required centuries for the major Christian religions to become comfortable that Earth was not at the center of the universe and 2) a century and a half have passed without acquiescence by most religions and people to the Darwinian explanation of human origin. Yet, we cannot dismiss the human capacity to believe both evidence-based understandings and unsupported convictions. After all, this duality was central to the survival of the *Endurance* Party. Shackleton believed absolutely that he would deliver his men to safety. Similarly, the men believed totally in Shackleton to do so. Yet, they equally believed evidence-based biological and physical reality.

Science like religion has delivered the good and the bad. It provided the key to a heaven-like existence that many have experienced, but that key also opened the door to a hellish existence for some in the past and perhaps for all humanity in the future. Through the application of science we have changed the climate, impacted virtually every ecosystem on Earth, created vast wastelands contaminated with our unique and toxic compounds, revised fire regimes and global hydrological cycles, and created nuclear and chemical weapons as well as developed biological weapons capable of extinguishing much of humankind. Science has also helped foster the emergence of an economically centered life that is too often one of meaningless affluence.

Science and religion, both of which are grounded in our evolved nature, have similar histories filled with the desirable and the undesirable. One might contend that this is the unavoidable tragedy of the way things have been and will be. Nevertheless, it falls to us to seek ways to create societies that embody the best while diminishing the less desirable of both.

§

A hundred years ago the *Endurance* Party sailed from South Georgia bound for Antarctica and "the largest and most striking of all journeys—the crossing of the continent." They did have the "most striking of all journeys"— one unparalleled to this day. I have attempted here to establish why it is a parable for the journey facing humanity.

Looking back on the *Endurance* Party's story, we can see how knowledge—both the acceptance of and absence of—altered the perspectives and plans of the leaders and crew. At the outset, Shackleton knew that the hull shape of the *Endurance* was ill-suited to Weddell Sea ice—he was even reminded of this fact by South Georgian whalers. However, he let money and the urgency of the mission trump this knowledge. When the *Endurance* became ice-locked early in 1915, it was clear to both leaders and crew that crossing Antarctica would not occur as planned. They were more disappointed than concerned. In July 1915, when Shackleton and his team anticipated the coming of the first major pressure event, the leaders recognized that their situation had changed for the worse—they knew it was likely that the ship would be crushed. Shackleton, Wild, and Worsley began adjusting to and planning for the loss of *Endurance*, while remaining confident that they could trek to land and rescue.

It took the second, third, and perhaps the fourth and final pressure event to convince the entire crew that the ship was doomed. Nevertheless, all still believed they were in charge of their fate. However, after the first trekking attempt, the leaders and many of the men realized it would be impossible to reach land by walking, although most still remained confident in affecting their fate. The second attempt in December 1915 removed all doubt of their dire straits. They were at the mercy of nature. All they could do was to prepare and respond well to what visited them. Of course, they were always at nature's mercy even though they believed otherwise until the second failed trek. In the end the *Endurance* Party embodied a combination of excellent leadership, cooperation, discipline, luck, and evidence-based decision making that saved the day. All were necessary: none alone was sufficient.

Humanity too is now in dire straits, unquestionably at the mercy of nature. Few believe this to be the case. However, we will have to behave as the Shackleton Party did to survive our self-imposed climate change and all the rest. Ours is a fantasy-creating species. We are able to imagine anything. Nevertheless, when it comes to making important decisions, we will have to use our moral compass to select from the best science available to bequeath future generations a livable planet.

Notes

Part 1: Story of the *Endurance* Party

I relied mostly on the following four books to write the *Endurance* Party's story. When I found differences in small details among these and other accounts of the *Endurance* story, I tended to use what Alfred Lansing had written in his 1959 book. I made this decision because it appeared to me that he had access to many diaries and other first hand material that others did not have. I could be wrong; however, my conclusions do not rely on these minor differences.

Lansing, A., Endurance: *Shackleton's Incredible Voyage* (New York: Caroll & Graf Publishers, 1959).

Shackleton, E., *South: The Last Antarctic Expedition of Shackleton and the* Endurance (New York: The Lyons Press, 1998).

Worsley, F.A., Endurance: *An Epic of Polar Adventure* (New York: Norton, 2000).

Worsley, F.A., *Shackleton's Boat Journey* (New York: Norton, 1987).

Other books I read or consulted to write the *Endurance* Party's story:

Alexander, C., The Endurance: *Shackleton's Legendary Antarctic Expedition* (New York: Knopf, 1999).

Armstrong, J., *Spirit of* Endurance: *The True Story of the Shackleton Expedition to the Antarctic* (New York: Crown Publishers, 2000).

Costigan, P. *et al.* (Contributors and Consultants), *South with* Endurance, *Shackleton's Antarctic Expedition 1914-1917, The Photographs of Frank Hurley* (New York: Simon & Schuster, 2001).

Fisher, M. and Fisher, J., *Shackleton and the Antarctic* (Boston: Houghton Mifflin, 1958).

Shackleton, E., *The Heart of the Antarctic: The Farthest South Expedition 1907-1909* (New York: New American Library, 2000).

Thomson, J., *Shackleton's Captain: A Biography of Frank Worsley* (Toronto: Mosaic Press, 1999).

Pg 1: Illustration for introduction to Part 1 is the beset *Endurance*, © Donald Watson illustration based on Frank Hurley photograph in Costigan *et al.*, *South with* Endurance, p. 103.

Chapter 1: Adrift in the Weddell Sea

Pg 3: Shackleton quotations ("She's going, boys!" and "She's gone, boys.") are from Shackleton, E., *South: The Last Antarctic Expedition of Shackleton and the* Endurance (New York: The Lyons Press, 1998), p. 98-99.

Shackleton quote ("There now remains ... crossing of the continent") is from Lansing, A., Endurance: *Shackleton's Incredible Voyage* (New York: Caroll & Graf Publishers, 1959), p. 11.

Pg 4: 1.1, © Donald Watson illustration.

Pg 5: Wild quote ("... [Shackleton] privately forced ... that one biscuit") from Worsley, F.A., *Shackleton's Boat Journey* (New York, Norton, 1987), Introduction by Hillary, p. 20-21.

Pg 6: Worsley quote ("He and I spent ... and that was that") from Worsley, F.A., Endurance: *An epic polar adventure* (New York: Norton, 2000), p. 15.

The ages of the men in the *Endurance* Party are given at http://en.wikipedia.org/wiki/Personnel_of_the_Imperial_Trans-Antarctic_Expedition [15 October 2013].

Pg 7: 1.2, © Donald Watson illustration based on 1914 sketch by Walter How, able seaman on the *Endurance*, in Thompson, J., *Shackleton's Captain: A Biography of Frank Worsley* (Toronto: Mosaic Press, 1999).

Pg 9: 1.3, © Donald Watson illustration based on Frank Hurley photograph of Stromness whaling station in Alexander, C., *The* Endurance: *Shackleton's Legendary Antarctic Expedition* (New York: Knopf, 1999), p. 18.

Pg 10: Worsley quote ("Great blocks of ice ... live through it") from Worsley, Endurance, p. 37.

Worsley quote ("There was a continual ... played upon us") from Worsley, Endurance, p. 46.

Worsley quote ("When you gazed ... known to you") from Worsely, Endurance, p. 47.

1.4, © Donald Watson illustration based on Frank Hurley photograph in Costigan, P. *et al.* (Contributors and Consultants), *South with* Endurance, *Shackleton's Antarctic Expedition 1914-1917, The Photographs of Frank Hurley* (New York: Simon & Schuster, 2001), p. 75.

Pg 11: Worsley quote ("We feel as ... beheld the Pacific") from Lansing, *Endurance*, p. 28.

1.5, © Donald Watson illustration based on Frank Hurley photograph in Costigan *et al.*, *South with* Endurance, p. 72.

Pg 13: 1.6, © Donald Watson illustration based on Frank Hurley photograph in Costigan *et al.*, *South with* Endurance, p. 84.

Worsley quote ("We heard tapping ... or turned over") from Shackleton, E., *South*, p. 40.

Pg 14: 1.7, © Donald Watson illustration based Frank Hurley photograph in Costigan *et al.*, *South with* Endurance, p. 103.

Pg 15: Shackleton quote ("Oh, I don't ... with the boys?") from Lansing, *Endurance*, p. 17.

Pg 17: 1.8, © Donald Watson illustration.

Lansing quote ("sweethearts and wives" and "May they never meet") from Lansing, *Endurance*, p. 43.

Pg 18: Worsley quote ("She's pretty near ... you are ready") from Worsley, *Endurance*, p. 3-6, modified and shortened.

Pg 19: Shackleton quote ("This crack was ... stress had begun") from Shackleton, *South*, p. 55-56.

Pg 20: 1.9, © Donald Watson illustration based on Frank Hurley photograph in Costigan *et al.*, *South with* Endurance, p. 132.

Lansing quote ("There once was ... that damned cat?") from Lansing, *Endurance*, p. 50.

Pg 21: Greenstreet quote ("coming out of ... jerks it gave") from Lansing, *Endurance*, p. 54.

Pg 22: Macklin quote ("The whole sensation ... big to grasp") from Lansing, *Endurance*, p. 57.

Pg 23: Wild quote ("She's going, boys. ... to get off") from Lansing, *Endurance*, p. 60.

Pg 24: 1.10, © Donald Watson illustration based on Frank Hurley photograph in Costigan *et al.*, *South with* Endurance, p. 167.

Pg 25: Shackleton quote ("The destruction and ... a hundred times") from Shackleton, *South*, p. 77.

Shackleton quote ("I must bend ... goes to ground") from Shackleton, *South*, p. 77.

Chapter 2: Living on the Floes

Pg 26: Shackleton quote ("with the life-giving drink") from Shackleton, E., *South: The Last Antarctic Expedition of Shackleton and the* Endurance (New York: The Lyons Press, 1998), p. 78.

Wild quote ("If any of ... put them outside!") from Shackleton, *South*, p. 78.

Pg 27: Lansing quote ("Each man, he ... of its [presumed] value") from Lansing, A., Endurance: *Shackleton's Incredible Voyage* (New York: Caroll & Graf Publishers, 1959), p. 64.

Queen Alexandra quote ("May the Lord help ... in the deep") from Lansing, Endurance, p. 62.

Book of Job quote ("Out of whose ... deep is frozen") from Lansing, Endurance, p. 65.

2.1, © Donald Watson illustration based on text in Lansing, Endurance, p. 64-65 and various Frank Hurley photographs in Costigan, P. *et al.* (Contributors and Consultants), *South with* Endurance, *Shackleton's Antarctic Expedition 1914-1917, The Photographs of Frank Hurley* (New York: Simon & Schuster, 2001).

Pg 28: 2.2, © Donald Watson illustration based on Frank Hurley photograph in Costigan *et al.*, *South with* Endurance, p. 174-175.

Pg 29: Worsley quote ("It is scandalous ... would tackle before") from Lansing, Endurance, p. 69-70.

Pg 31: 2.3, © Donald Watson illustration based Frank Hurley photograph in Costigan *et al.*, *South with* Endurance, p. 176-177.

Pg 32: Shackleton quote ("I cannot write about it") from Lansing, Endurance, p. 83.

Macklin quote ("Really, this sort ... it all tomorrow!") from Lansing, Endurance, p. 85.

Shackleton quote ("Am thinking of starting off for the west") from Lansing, Endurance, p. 89.

Greenstreet quote ("... the going will ... the idea directly") from Lansing, Endurance, p. 89-90.

Worsley quote ("My idea is ... of our journey...") from Lansing, Endurance, p. 90.

Macklin quote ("... personally I think ... want to go") from Lansing, Endurance, p. 90.

Pg 33: Shackleton quote ("Endurance crushed and … 1915. E. H. Shackleton") from Worsley, F.A., Endurance: *An Epic of Polar Adventure* (New York: Norton, 2000), p. 55.

Shackleton quote ("to perform any … master and owner") from Lansing, Endurance, p. 95.

Pg 34: Shackleton quote ("Turned in but … of strain & stress") from Lansing, Endurance, p. 96.

Pg 35: 2.4, © Donald Watson illustration.

Shackleton quote ("I suppose it is the strain. … rest, free from thought") from Lansing, Endurance, p. 104.

Pg 36: Greenstreet quote ("[T]he present shortage … here we are") from Lansing, Endurance, p. 105.

2.5, © Donald Watson illustration based on Frank Hurley photograph in Costigan *et al.*, *South with* Endurance, p. 279.

Pg 37: Greenstreet quote ("For the first … all over again") from Lansing, Endurance, p. 117.

Pg 38: Greenstreet quote ("Day passes day … being absolutely exhausted") from Lansing, Endurance, p. 117.

Shackleton quote: ("It will do …are too big!") from Lansing, Endurance, p. 121.

Pg 39: Shackleton quote ("Land in sight! Land in sight!") from Lansing, Endurance, p. 123.

Lansing quote ("Crack! Lash up and stow!") from Lansing, Endurance, p. 188.

Pg 40: Macklin quote ("[We want to] be off this … forces of nature") from Lansing, Endurance, p. 135.

Pg 41: Shackleton quote ("I confess that … expectation of success") from Shackleton, *South*, p. 120.

Shackleton quote ("Strike the tents and clear the boats!") from Lansing, Endurance, p. 137.

Shackleton quote ("Launch the boats") from Lansing, Endurance, p. 138.

Chapter 3: Reaching Land

Pg 44: 3.1, © Donald Watson illustration based on text in Lansing, A., Endurance: *Shackleton's Incredible Voyage* (New York: Caroll & Graf Publishers, 1959), p. 148-152 and various Frank Hurley images in Costigan, P. *et al.*

(Contributors and Consultants), *South with* Endurance, *Shackleton's Antarctic Expedition 1914-1917, The Photographs of Frank Hurley* (New York: Simon & Schuster, 2001).

Pg 45: Shackleton quote ("A chance is coming" but then, "No") from Lansing, Endurance, p. 151.

Pg 46: Worsely and Shackleton quotes ("30 miles astern, sir" [Worsley], "We haven't done as well as we expected" [Shackleton]) from Worsley, F.A., *Shackleton's Boat Journey* (New York: Norton, 1987), p. 47.

Pg 47: Marston and Shackleton quotes ("All right ... some dry mitts" [Marston], "I left a pair ... tell'em I'm coming" [Shackleton]) from Worsley, *Shackleton's Boat Journey*, p. 54.

Pg 49: Worsley quote ("For God's sake ... Hoist sail!") from Lansing, Endurance, p. 171.

Pg 50: Worsley quote ("Then I saw ... twenty minutes later") from Worsley, *Shackleton's Boat Journey*, p. 83.

3.2, © Donald Watson illustration based on various Frank Hurley photographs in Costigan *et al.*, *South with* Endurance.

Chapter 4: Sailing the Drake Passage

Pg 52: James quote ("Turned in and ... croaking of the penguins") from Lansing, A., Endurance: *Shackleton's Incredible Voyage* (New York: Caroll & Graf Publishers, 1959), p. 179.

Pg 53: Maklin quote ("A more inhospitable ... of shelter anywhere") from Lansing, Endurance, p. 185.

Pg 55: Shackleton quote ("You can convey ... tried my best") from Lansing, Endurance, p. 191.

Pg 56: 4.1, © Donald Watson illustration based on Frank Hurley photograph in Costigan, P. et al. (Contributors and Consultants), *South with* Endurance, *Shackleton's Antarctic Expedition 1914-1917, The Photographs of Frank Hurley* (New York: Simon & Schuster, 2001), p. 192-193.

Orde-Lees quote ("They made surprising ... sail and all") from Lansing, Endurance, p. 195.

Pg 57: Hurley quote ("Life here without ... almost beyond endurance") from Lansing, Endurance, p. 197.

Macklin quote ("Everything deeply snowed ... had sought shelter") from Lansing, Endurance, p. 197.

Pg 58: Blackborow quote ("I'd like a cigarette") from Lansing, Endurance, p. 207.

Greenstreet quote ("Everyone spent the … goddam rotten day") from Lansing, Endurance, p. 205.

Pg 59: Orde-Lees quote ("One cannot help … really do think") from Lansing, Endurance, p. 203.

Lansing quote ("that every scrap … to Deception Island") from Lansing, Endurance, p. 214.

4.2, © Donald Watson illustration based on various Frank Hurley photographs in Costigan et al., *South with* Endurance.

Pg 60: Worsley quote ("All the strange … blue shadows above") from Worsley, F.A., *Shackleton's Boat Journey* (New York: Norton, 1987), p. 105.

Shackleton and Worsley quotes ("No," Worsley replied, "Not a chance." [Worsley] "Do you know I know nothing about boat sailing?" [Shackleton], "All right, Boss." … "I do." [Worsley]) combined from Lansing, Endurance, p. 221 and Worsley, *Shackleton's Boat Journey*, p. 106-07.

Pg 61: 4.3, © Donald Watson illustration based on text in Lansing, Endurance, p. 148-152 and various Frank Hurley images in Costigan *et al.*, *South with* Endurance.

Pg 62: Worsley quote ("talked of going … hundred-ton sailing craft") from Worsley, *Shackleton's Boat Journey*, p. 111.

Worsley quote ("Halfway through you … order of march") from Worsley, *Shackleton's Boat Journey*, p. 110

Darwin quote ("The sight … peril and shipwreck") from Lansing, Endurance, p. 225-226.

Pg 65: McCarthy quote ("It's a grand day sir") from Lansing, Endurance, p. 235.

Lansing quote ("The sight that … soaking in salt water") from Lansing, Endurance, p. 236.

Lansing quote ("And all of them … outing of some sort") from Lansing, Endurance, p. 236.

Pg 66: Shackleton quote ("For God's sake … It's got us!") from Lansing, Endurance, p. 238.

Pg 67: 4.4, © Donald Watson illustration based on various Frank Hurley photographs in Costigan *et al.*, *South with* Endurance.

Worsley quote ("Most unfavorable conditions … jumping like a flea") from Lansing, Endurance, p. 241.

Pg 68: McCarthy quote ("Land ho!") from Worsley, *Shackleton's Boat Journey*, p. 140.

Shackleton quote ("We've done it. … off Elephant Island") from Worsley, *Shackleton's Boat Journey*, p. 140.

Pg 69: Worsley quote ("The sky all … man to save") from Worsley, *Shackleton's Boat Journey*, p. 143-144.

Pg 70: Lansing quote ("Worsley thought to himself of the pity of it all." … "was now stowed in the forepeak … how terribly close they had come") from Lansing, Endurance, p. 251.

Lansing quote ("She's clearing it! She's clearing it!") from Lansing, Endurance, p. 251.

Chapter 5: Crossing South Georgia

Pg 75: 5.1, Worsley rough memory map of trek across South Georgia Island from Shackleton, E., *South: The Last Antarctic Expedition of Shackleton and the Endurance* (New York: The Lyons Press, 1998), p. 207.

Shackleton quote ("We'll try it") from Worsley, F.A., *Shackleton's Boat Journey* (New York: Norton, 1987), p. 198.

Pg 76: 5.2, © Donald Watson illustration based on text in Lansing, A., Endurance: *Shackleton's Incredible Voyage* (New York: Caroll & Graf Publishers, 1959), p. 263-267.

Pg 77: Shackleton quote ("Can we stay here?") from Lansing, Endurance, p. 267 (not a direct quote).

Lansing quote ("They seemed to … faster—down … down … down!") from Lansing, Endurance, p. 267.

Crean quote ("Holy smoke, look at the Skipper's mouth!") from Worsley, *Shackleton's Boat Journey*, p. 200.

Pg 78: Shackelton quote ("Never did music … as that whistle") from Worsley, *Shackleton's Boat Journey*, p. 206.

Worsley quote ("Yoicks! Tallyho!") from Worsley, *Shackleton's Boat Journey*, p. 206.

Shackleton quote ("No, we'll try it") from Worsley, *Shackleton's Boat Journey*, p. 207.

Pg 79: Shackleton quote (Shackleton quietly said, "Let's go down") from Lansing, Endurance, p. 271.

Worsley quote ("[r]agged, filthy … for seven months") from Worsley, *Shackleton's Boat Journey*, p. 212.

Pg 80: Foreman, Sørelle and Shackleton quotes ("There are three funny-looking … My name is Shackleton") combined from Shackleton, *South*, p. 206 and Lansing, Endurance, p. 274.

5.3, © Donald Watson illustration.

Pg 82: Shackleton quote ("There are only ... are all saved!") from Worsley, Endurance, p. 179.

Part 2: Why Did the *Endurance* Party Survive?

Pg 83: Illustration for introduction to Part 2 is the rescue from Elephant Island, © Donald Watson illustration based on Frank Hurley photographs in Costigan, P. *et al.* (Contributors and Consultants), *South with* Endurance, *Shackleton's Antarctic Expedition 1914-1917, The Photographs of Frank Hurley* (New York: Simon & Schuster, 2001), p. 304.

Chapter 6: Message from the Endurance Party's Survival

Pg 86: Worsley quote ("If it comes to ... of any length") from Lansing, A., Endurance: *Shackleton's Incredible Voyage* (New York: Caroll & Graf Publishers, 1959), p. 111.

Pg 87: Shackleton quote ("Launch the boats. ... any old way") from Lansing, Endurance, p. 152.

Pg 88: Shackleton ("... through a rift in ... could have saved us") from Shackleton, E., *South: The Last Antarctic Expedition of Shackleton and the* Endurance (New York: The Lyons Press, 1998), p. 177-178.

Lansing quote ("That night Shackleton wrote, almost timorously, ... '...when commenting thereon'") from Lansing, Endurance, p. 108.

Pg 89: Shackleton quote ("The ice moves ... the higher Power") from Shackleton, *South*, p. 80-81.

Worsley quote ("I learnt afterwards ... both Shackleton and Crean") from Worsley, F.A., Endurance: *An Epic of Polar Adventure* (New York: Norton, 2000), p. 164.

Lansing quote ("[Shackleton] reached under his ... and walked away") from Lansing, Endurance, p. 64-65.

Pg 90: Shackleton quote ("...what the ice gets ... the ice keeps") from Worsley, Endurance, p. 3-4.

Lansing quote ("For some men ... supplies and instruments") from Lansing, Endurance, p. 65.

Pg 91: Worsley quote ("Nevertheless, he encouraged ... important geographical discoveries") from Worsley, Endurance, p. 54-55.

Worsley quote ("...barrier cliffs thrown up ... all is deep sea") from Worsley, Endurance, p. 47.

Worsley quote ("We are ready to ... much of food") from Lansing, Endurance, p. 70.

Accounts of the Greenland Norse are found in Seaver, K., *The Frozen Echo* (Redwood City, CA: Stanford University Press, 1966) and Pringle, H., "Death in Norse Greenland," *Science* 275 (1997), p. 924-926.

Pg 92:   Worsley quote ("[If] we did not ... between hunger and cold") from Worsley, Endurance, p. 66.

Shackleton quote ("Launch the boats") from Lansing, Endurance, p. 138.

Part 3: Nature's Rules and Decision Making

Pg 93:   Illustration for introduction to Part 3 is of two sled dogs and meteorologist Hussey, © Donald Watson illustration based on Frank Hurley photograph in Costigan, P. *et al.* (Contributors and Consultants), *South with Endurance, Shackleton's Antarctic Expedition 1914-1917, The Photographs of Frank Hurley* (New York: Simon & Schuster, 2001), p. 277. The image illustrates biophilia or love of life. Biophilia has been part of human nature for a very long time, but first introduced formally through a personal story of discovery by Wilson, E.O., *Biophilia: The Human Bond with Other Species* (Cambridge, MA: Harvard University Press, 1984).

Chapter 7: Nature's Rules

The basic science presented here can be found in college introductory science textbooks. Introductory biology textbooks like Raven, P.H. *et al.*, *Biology*, 9th edition (New York: McGraw Hill, 2011) consider biological rules and most of the biology presented here.

Pg 97:   Many excellent web sites and general audience books focus on human evolution including: The American Museum of Natural History (http://www.amnh.org/exhibitions/past-exhibitions/human-origins/the-history-of-human-evolution [accessed 14 October 2013]), The Smithsonian Institute (http://humanorigins.si.edu/resources/intro-human-evolution [accessed 14 September 2013]), (http://en.wikipedia.org/wiki/Human_evolution [accessed 14 October 2013]) and general audience books on human evolution are given by Good Reads (http://www.goodreads.com/shelf/show/human-evolution [accessed 14 September 2013]).

A general discussion of our evolutionary history including the genetic roots of human nature are found in Wade, N., *Before the Dawn: Recovering the Lost History of Our Ancestors* (New York: Penguin, 2006).

Morrison quote ("[T]he brain is … evolutionary and genetic origins") from Morrison, R., *The Spirit in the Gene: Humanity's Proud Illusion and the Laws of Nature* (Ithaca, NY: Cornell University Press, 1999), p. xiii.

Pg 100: Wilson quote ("The relative indifference … difficult to marshal") from Wilson, E.O., *The Future of Life* (New York: Knopf, 2002), p. 40.

Evidence for the extent of human evolutionary selection pressure is given in Palumbi, S.R., "Humans as the world's greatest evolutionary force," *Science* 239 (2001), p. 1786–1790.

Chapter 8: Climate Change

Among the many informative general audience books on climate change published over the past 25 years are McKibben, B., *The End of Nature* (New York: Random House, 1989); Schneider, S.H., *Global Warming: Are We Entering the Greenhouse Century?* (San Francisco: Sierra Club Books, 1989); Schneider, S.H., *Laboratory Earth: The Planetary Gamble We Can't Afford to Lose* (New York: Basic Books, 1997); Weart, S.R., *The Discovery of Global Warming* (Cambridge, MA: Harvard University Press, 2003); Flannery, T., *The Weather Makers: How Man Is Changing the Climate and What It Means for Life on Earth* (New York: Atlantic Monthly Press, 2005); Hansen, J., *Storms of My Grandchildren: The Truth about the Coming Climate Catastrophe and Our Last Chance to Save Humanity* (New York: Bloomsbury USA, 2009); McKibben, B., *Eaarth: Making a Life on a Tough New Planet* (New York: Times Books, 2010); Alley, R., *The Two-Mile Time Machine: Ice Cores, Abrupt Climate Change, and Our Future* (Princeton, NJ: Princeton University Press, 2011); Climate Central, *Global Weirdness: Severe Storms, Deadly Heat Waves, Relentless Drought, Rising Seas and the Weather of the Future* (New York: Pantheon, 2012).

Among the many websites on climate change the following three are especially useful for understanding climate science: global warming topic on Wikipedia provides a detailed discussion and references (http://en.wikipedia.org/wiki/Global_Warming [accessed 21 March 2013]); Science Daily is an excellent source for the latest, scientific-based articles on climate change (www.sciencedaily.com [accessed 21 March 2013]); and Climate Central is an excellent website for the latest information on climate change (www.climatecentral.org [accessed 21 March 2013]).

The large number of climate change doubters in the general public of the United States can be explained, in part, by intentional and well funded campaigns to raise doubt about the validity of climate science. Discussion of these campaigns can be found in PBS, 23 October 2012, *Frontline* documentary *Climate of Doubt* (http://www.pbs.org/wgbh/pages/frontline/climate-of-doubt/ [accessed 21 March 2013]); Oreskes, N. and Conway, E.M., *Merchants of Death: How a Handful of Scientists Obscured the Truth on Issues from Tobacco Smoke to Global Warming* (New York: Bloomsbury Press, 2010); Powell, J., *The Inquisition of Climate Science* (New York: Columbia University Press, 2011) and 16 years earlier in Gelbspan, R., *The Heat is ON: The High Stakes Battle over Earth's Threatened Climate* (Reading, MA: Addison-Wesley, 1997) with updates online (http://www.heatisonline.org/main.cfm [accessed 22 March 2013]).

Pg 101:   The atmospheric concentration of CO_2 reached 400 ppm in May 2013 (http://blogs.scientificamerican.com/observations/2013/05/09/400-ppm-carbon-dioxide-in-the-atmosphere-reaches-prehistoric-levels/ [accessed 13 October 2013]).

Arrhenius, S., "On the influence of the carbonic acid in the air upon the temperature of the ground," *Philosophical Magazine and Journal of Science* 41 (1896), p. 237–276. Arrhenius's analyses demonstrated a several degree temperature increase for a doubling of atmospheric CO_2 concentration that is similar to those of the IPCC fourth report in 2007 (http://en.wikipedia.org/wiki/IPCC_Fourth_Assessment_Report [accessed 21 March 2013]).

Keeling Curve data found at http://scrippsco2.ucsd.edu/ [accessed 5 October 2013] and http://www.climatecentral.org/gallery/graphics/keeling_curve [accessed 5 October 2013].

Pg 102:   8.1, © Donald Watson illustration based on measurements of atmospheric CO_2 concentration at the top of Mauna Loa on the island of Hawaii given at http://scrippsco2.ucsd.edu/ [accessed 5 October 2013] and http://www.climatecentral.org/gallery/graphics/keeling_curve [accessed 5 October 2013].

Hansen quote ("'Loading' of the climate … the land area") from Hansen, J., Sato, M., and Ruedy, R., "Perception of climate change," *Proceedings of the National Academy of Sciences* (United States) (2012), p. 4, www.pnas,org/cgi/doi/10.1073/pnas.1205276109 [accessed 4 October 2013].

Pg 103:   A recent publication extends what Hansen and colleagues concluded about the planet getting hotter fast. The paper projects "the year when the projected mean climate of a given location moves to a state continuously outside the bounds of historical variability under alternative greenhouse gas emissions scenarios. Using 1860 to 2005 as the historical period, this index has a global mean of 2069 (± 18 years s.d.) for near-surface air temperature under an emissions stabilization scenario and 2047 (± 14 years s.d.) under a 'business-as-usual' scenario." That is, it will take between 34 and 56 years until the new average lows will exceed the average historical highs; Mora, C. *et al.*, "The projected timing of climate departure from recent variability," *Nature* 502 (10 October 2013), p. 183–187, http://www.nature.com/nature/journal/v502/n7470/full/nature12540.html [accessed 14 October 2013].

Pg 104: 8.2, © Donald Watson illustration based on data of James Hansen and colleagues (Hansen et al., "Perception of climate change") and Satterfield, D., http://blogs.agu.org/wildwildscience/2012/08/10/nasa-climate-expert-james-hansen-an-amazing-forecast/ [accessed 4 October 2013].

Pg 105: Extremely hot summer temperatures experienced in Australia found in Hannam, P., "Temperatures off the charts as Australia turns deep purple," *The Sydney Morning Herald*, 8 January 2013, http://www.smh.com.au/environment/weather/temperatures-off-the-charts-as-australia-turns-deep-purple-20130108-2ce33.html [accessed 13 October 2013].

New colors in weather prediction map of The Bureau of Meteorology (Australia) given in Special Climate Statement 43 — Extreme Heat in January 2013, updated 25 January 2013, http://www.bom.gov.au/climate/current/statements/scs43d.pdf [accessed 13 October 2013].

8.3, Earth-sun relationship © Donald Watson from Watson, D. and Adams, M., *Design for Flooding: Resilience to Climate Change* (New York: John Wiley, 2011) p. 10, by permission.

Pg 106: McKibben, *End of Nature* Schneider quotation ("I do believe … if not sooner") from Schneider, S.H. and Mesirow, L., *The Genesis Strategy: Climate and Global Survival* (New York: Plenum, 1976), p. 11.

Hansen quotation ("Number one, the earth … summer heat waves") from "The greenhouse effect: impacts on current global temperature and regional heat waves," Testimony of James Hansen, United States Senate, Committee on Energy and Natural Resources, 23 June 1988, http://image.guardian.co.uk/sys-files/Environment/documents/2008/06/23/ClimateChangeHearing1988.pdf [accessed 4 October 2013].

Information on establishment and composition of Intergovernmental Panel on Climate Change from Enzler, S.M., "History of the greenhouse effect and global warming," http://www.lenntech.com/greenhouse-effect/global-warming-history.htm#ixzz2Jao9CQQw [accessed 13 October 2013].

Among credible climate scientists more than 98% affirm that climate change is happening and that it is human caused (Anderegg, W.R.L., Prall, J.W., Harold, J., and Schneider, S.H., "Expert credibility in climate," (http://www.pnas.org/content/early/2010/06/04/1003187107.full.pdf+html [accessed 21 March 2013]). The latest report of the Intergovernmental

Panel on Climate Change states that it is extremely likely (95% confident) that the observed warming is human caused (http://www.climate-change2013.org/images/uploads/WGIAR5-SPM_Approved27Sep2013.pd f [accessed 14 October 2013]).

Pg 107: Prediction of significant costs to the economy if we were to move away from fossil fuels is given in Nordhaus, W.D. and Boyer, J., *Warming the World: Economic Models of Global Warming* (Cambridge, MA: MIT Press, 2000). A response in 2002 to the economists' assessment that reducing carbon dioxide emissions is too expensive is given in Azar, C. and Schneider, S.H., "Are the economic costs of stabilizing the atmosphere prohibitive?," *Ecological Economics* 42 (2002), p. 73-80.

Different perspectives of biologists and mainstream economists is considered by McDaniel, C.N., *Wisdom for a Livable Planet: The Visionary Work of Terri Swearingen, Dave Foreman, Wes Jackson, Helena Norberg-Hodge, Werner Fornos, Herman Daly, Stephen Schneider, and David Orr* (San Antonio, TX: Trinity University Press, 2005), Chapter 8: Accepting uncertainty: Stephen Schneider and global climate change, p. 164-190.

Pg 108: Current information on status of climate change given in The Fifth Report of Working Group 1 of the Intergovernmental Panel on Climate Change, http://www.climatechange2013.org/images/uploads/WGIAR5-SPM_Approved27Sep2013.pdf [accessed 14 October 2013].

8.4, © Donald Watson illustration. Not to scale. The melting of the Antarctic ice cap is a possibility on our current trajectory of increased heat-trapping gases as discussed in Ward, P.D., *The Flooded Earth: Our Future in a World without Ice Caps* (New York: Basic Books, 2010).

Chapter 9: Biodiversity and Life Support

Over the past 60 years many excellent books have been written on biodiversity and its relevance to human wellbeing and that of all life. The two most cited environmental books as seminal in raising a person's environmental awareness and concerns for life are Leopold, A., *A Sand County Almanac and Sketches Here and There* (New York: Oxford University Press, 1949) and Carson, R., *Silent Spring* (Boston: Houghton Mifflin, 1962). An overall perspective on the history of human relationships with life in the broadest sense is given in Ponting, C., *A Green History of the World: The Rise and Collapse of Great Civilizations* (New York: Penguin Books, 1991) and the revised edition published in 2007. Among the best and most accessible books explaining the origin of biological diversity and the human impact on biodiversity is Wilson, E.O., *The Diversity of Life* (Cambridge, MA: Harvard University Press, 1992).

Over the past two decades other excellent books on biodiversity and life support include: Noss, R. and Cooperrider, A., *Saving Nature's Legacy* (Washington, DC: Island Press, 1994); Flannery, T., *The Future Eaters: An Ecological History of the Australian Lands and People* (Port Melbourne: Reed Books, 1995); Daily, G.C., *Nature's Services: Societal Dependence on Natural Ecosystems* (Washington, DC: Island Press, 1997); Baskin, Y., *The Work of Nature: How the Diversity of Life Sustains Us* (Washington, DC: Island Press, 1997); Terborge, J., *Requiem for Nature* (Washington, DC: Island Press, 1999); Stein, B.A., Kutner, L.S., and Adams, J.S. (Eds), *Precious Heritage: The Status of Biodiversity in the United States* (Oxford: Oxford University Press, 2000); Flannery, T., *The Eternal Frontier: An Ecological History of North America and Its People* (New York: Atlantic Monthly Press, 2001); Wilson, E.O., *The Future of Life* (New York: Knopf, 2002); Ellis, R., *The Empty Ocean: Plundering the World's Marine Life* (Washington DC: Island Press, 2003).

Pg 111: 9.1 © Donald Watson illustration based on Frank Hurley photograph in Costigan, P. *et al.* (Contributors and Consultants), *South with* Endurance, *Shackleton's Antarctic Expedition 1914-1917, The Photographs of Frank Hurley* (New York: Simon & Schuster, 2001), p. 277.

The hunter-gatherer pattern of life that comprised more than 95% of human existence and during which time our core human behaviors evolved and we lived off the bounty of the land is considered in Lee, R.B., *The Dobe !Kung* (Fort Worth, TX: Harcourt Brace Jovanovich, 1984); Bates, E., *The Native Tribes of Western Australia* (Canberra: National Library of Australia, 1985); Gowdy, J. (Ed.), *Limited Wants, Unlimited Means: A Hunter-Gatherer Reader on Economics and the Environment* (Washington, DC: Island Press, 1998).

Extinctions correlated with humanity's arrival on continents and islands are found in Wilson, *The Diversity of Life* and *The Future of Life.*

On the Hawaiian Island 17 species disappeared after European arrival from Wilson, *The Diversity of Life*, p. 245-246.

European caused mammalian extinctions and Red Listed species in Australia from Wilson, *The Future of Life*, p. 91.

Pg 112: Extinction of the great auk and 450 more species in the United States from Stein, Kutner, and Adams, *Precious Heritage*, p. 114.

Critically imperiled, imperiled, or vulnerable species in the United States from Stein, Kutner, and Adams, *Precious Heritage*, p. 101-104.

Wilson quote ("So important are … a few months") from Wilson, *The Diversity of Life*, p. 133.

ICUN Red List for world's mammals and status given in http://www.iuc-nredlist.org/initiatives/mammals/analysis [accessed 14 October 2013].

Czech results on reasons for putting the species on Endangered Species List as of 1995 from Czech, B. and Krausman, P.R., "Distribution and causation of species endangerment in the United States," *Science* 277 (1997), p. 1116-1117, http://www.sciencemag.org/content/277/5329/1116.full#ref-4 [accessed 15 October 2013].

Czech quote (… "urbanization, agriculture, outdoor … Endangered Species Act [ESA])" from Czech, B., *Shoveling Fuel for a Runaway Train* (Berkeley, CA: University of California Press, 2000), p. 50.

An insightful book on our ancestors' views of and actions in the natural world is Suzuki, D. and Knudtson, P., *Wisdom of the Elders: Sacred Native Stories of Nature* (New York: Bantam, 1992).

Pg 113: History of the American bison given in Dary, D.A., *The Buffalo Book: The Full Saga of the American Animal* (Athens, OH: Swallow Press/Ohio University Press, 1989).

History of human influences on biodiversity given in Wilson, *The Diversity of Life*, p. 42-78.

Explanations of weather, the flow of energy from the sun, and other natural forces as well as human activities that are influencing weather and all life are given in NOVA — *Earth From Space,* http://video.pbs.org/video/2334144059/ [accessed 14 October 2013].

Information on fires and logging roads in the Amazon rainforest given in http://en.wikipedia.org/wiki/Deforestation_of_the_Amazon_Rainforest [accessed 5 October 2013].

Information on Aral Sea given in http://geography.netscype.com/article/aral-sea-interesting-facts and http://en.wikipedia.org/wiki/Aral_Sea [accessed 5 October 2013].

Pg 114: History of the Adirondack Park given in Schneider, P., *The Adirondacks: A History of America's First Wilderness* (New York: Henry Holt and Company, 1997).

Data on United States National Parks are found in http://www.nps.gov/faqs.htm [accessed 17 March 2013].

Data on National Forest Service areas are found in http://www.fs.fed.us/land/staff/lar/LAR2011/LAR2011_Book_A5.pdf [accessed 15 October 2013] and http://en.wikipedia.org/wiki/United_States_National_Forest [accessed 15 October 2013].

Data on protected land area in United States and the world are found in http://en.wikipedia.org/wiki/Protected_areas_of_the_United_States [accessed 15 October 2013].

Information on and discussion of the Endangered Species Act given in Wilson, *The Future of Life*, p. 185-187.

Pg 115: Information on conservation strategies given in Foreman, D. and Wolke, H., *The Big Outside: A Description Inventory of the Big Wilderness Areas of the United States*, revised edition (New York: Harmony Books, 1992); Noss and Cooperrider, *Saving Nature's Legacy*; Soulé, M.E. and Terborgh, J. (Eds), *Continental Conservation: Scientific Foundations of Regional Reserve Networks* (Washington, DC: Island Press, 1999); Maehr, D., Noss, R., and Larkin, J. (Eds), *Large Mammal Restoration* (Washington, DC: Island Press, 2001); Foreman, D., *Rewilding North America: A Conservation Vision for the 21st Century* (Washington, DC: Island Press, 2004).

The Wildlands Network is described in http://www.twp.org/wildways [accessed 4 October 2013].

Pg 116: 9.2, © Donald Watson illustration based on Wildlands Network diagram of North American Wildways (http://www.twp.org/wildways [accessed 4 October 2013]).

Leopold quotes ("When the sun … path to the Gulf", "He leadeth me … like a premature snowstorm") from Leopold, *A Sand County Almanac*, p. 141-142.

Pg 117: Postel quote ("Today, the Colorado … south of the border") from http://articles.latimes.com/2012/mar/25/opinion/la-oe-postel-colorado-river-delta-20120325 [accessed 15 October 2013].

Chapter 10: Human Population

Over the past 200 years important essays have been written about the growth of the human population including Thomas Malthus (1830), Julian Huxley (1955), and Frederick Osborn (1960) found in *Three Essays on Population* (New York: New American Library, Mentor Book, 1960). Malthus's first article, "Essay on the Principle of Population," was first published in 1798.

Numerous books have been written on the human population and successful programs for reducing fertility rates including Ehrlich, P.R., *The Population Bomb* (New York: Ballantine, 1968); Fornos, W., *Gaining People, Losing Ground* (Ephrata, PA: Science Press, 1987); Ehrlich, P.R. and Ehrlich, A.H., *The Population Explosion* (New York: Touchstone, 1990); Brown, L.R., *Who Will Feed China: Wake-up Call for a Small Planet* (New York: W.W. Norton, 1995); Cohen, J.E., *How Many People Can the*

Earth Support? (New York: Norton, 1995); McKibben, B., *Maybe One: A Case for Smaller Families* (New York: Plume, 1999); Foreman, D., *Man Swarm and the Killing of Wildlife* (Durango, CO: Raven's Eye Press, 2011).

Consumption is the other side of human population growth and the subject of many books including Wackernagel, M. and Rees, W., *Our Ecological Footprint: Reducing Human Impact on the Earth* (Gabriola Island, BC: New Society Publishers, 1996); Ehrlich, P.R. and Ehrlich, A.H., *One with Nineveh: Politics, Consumption, and the Human Future* (Washington, DC: Island Press, 2004); Meadows, D.H., Randers, J., and Meadows, D.L., *Limits to Growth: The 30-Year Update* (White River Junction, VT: Chelsea Green Publishing, 2004).

Pg 118: The human population of 7 billion is larger than any other land animal weighing more than 110 pounds, from Wilson, E.O., *The Diversity of Life* (Cambridge, MA: Harvard University Press, 1992) p. 272.

Information on patterns of population growth can be found in Raven, P.H. *et al.*, *Biology*, 9th edition (New York: McGraw Hill, 2011), p. 145-166.

Pg 119: Malthus, Huxley, and Osborn, *Three Essays on Population.*

10.1, © Donald Watson illustration.

Pg 120: Ehrlich, *The Population Bomb.*

Analysis of the impact of population and consumption growth on resources in the 20th century along with the conclusion that it cannot be repeated in the 21st century are given in McNeill, J.R., *Something New Under the Sun: An Environmental History of the Twentieth-Century World* (New York: W.W. Norton, 2000).

Consumption is discussed in Durning, A., *How Much Is Enough?: The Consumer Society and the Future of the Earth* (New York: Norton, 1992).

The trends in resources, food, pollution, population, and other environmental issues over the past three decades can be found in the following annual publications: Worldwatch Institute, *State of the World, 1984–2014* (New York: W.W. Norton, 1984–2014); and Worldwatch Institute, *Vital Signs, 1992–2014* (New York: W.W. Norton, 1992–2014).

World fertility rate from http://data.worldbank.org/indicator/ SP.DYN.TFRT.IN and http://www.tradingeconomics.com/world/contraceptive-prevalence-percent-of-women-ages-15-49-wb-data.html [accessed 16 October 2013].

Pg 121: World contraceptive use from http://data.worldbank.org/indicator /SP.DYN.CONU.ZS and http://www.tradingeconomics.com/world/contraceptive-prevalence-percent-of-women-ages-15-49-wb-data.html [accessed 16 October 2013].

The consequences of pushing the Malthusian trap into the future are considered in Brown, L.R., Gardner, G., and Halweil, B., *Beyond Malthus: Nineteen Dimensions of the Population Challenge* (New York: Norton, 1999).

Quotation from the cover letter of Commission on Population and the American Future to President Nixon ("We have looked for ... of the average person") from http://www.mnforsustain.org/rockefeller _1972_transmittal_ltr_members_staff.htm [accessed 15 October 2013].

Chapter 11: Economic System and Resources

The details on the content of the economics currently taught and practiced can be found in college economics textbooks exemplified by Samuelson, P.A. and Nordhaus, W., *Economics* (New York: McGraw/Irwin, 2009). An alternative perspective for teaching and doing economics is given in Daly, H. and Farley, J., *Ecological Economics* (Washington, DC: Island Press, 2004).

Many excellent books have been written on the problems of neoclassical economics (our current economic system) including Daly, H.E. and Cobb, Jr, J.B., *For the Common Good: Redirecting the Economy toward the Environment and a Sustainable Future*, 2nd edition (Boston: Beacon Press, 1994); Hawken, P., Lovins, A., and Lovins, L.H., *Natural Capitalism: Creating the Next Industrial Revolution* (Boston: Little, Brown, 1999); Czech, B., *Shoveling Fuel for a Runaway Train: Errant Economists, Shameful Spenders, and a Plan to Stop Them All* (Berkeley: University of California Press, 2000); Barnes, P., *Who Owns the Sky? Our Common Assets and the Future of Capitalism* (Washington, DC: Island Press, 2001); Brown, L., *Eco-Economy: Building an Economy for the Earth* (New York: W.W. Norton, 2001); McKibben, B., *Deep Economy: The Wealth of Communities and the Durable Future* (New York: Times Books, 2007).

Many books argue that the current global political-market economic system is not grounded in the rules of the natural sciences and that as currently practiced this economic system does not have the capacity to preserve that which is of value for the wellbeing of humans and life on Earth. These books include Schumacher, E.F., *Small Is Beautiful: Economics as if People Mattered* (New York: Harper & Row, 1973); Power, T.M., *The Economic Pursuit of Quality* (New York: M.E. Sharpe, 1988); Henderson, H., *Paradigms in Progress: Life Beyond Economics* (San Francisco: Berrett-Koehler Publishers, 1995); Gowdy, J. and O'Hara, S., *Economic Theory for Environmentalists* (Delray Beach, FL: St Lucie Press, 1995); Nattrass, B. and Altomare, M., *The Natural Step for Business: Wealth, Ecology, and the Evolutionary Corporation* (Gabriola Island, BC: New Society Publishers, 1999); McDaniel, C.N. and Gowdy, J.M., *Paradise for Sale: A Parable of Nature* (Berkeley, CA: University of California Press, 2000); Davidson, E.A., *You Can't Eat GNP: Economics as if Ecology Mattered* (Cambridge, MA: Perseus Publishing, 2000); Brown, L.R., *Eco-Economy: Building an Economy for the Earth* (New York: Norton, 2001); Ellis, R., *The Empty Ocean* (Washington, DC: Island Press, 2003); Daly, H. and Farley, J., *Ecological Economics* (Washington, DC: Island Press, 2004); McDaniel, C.N., *Wisdom for a Livable Planet: The Visionary Work of Terri Swearingen, Dave Foreman, Wes Jackson, Helena Norberg-Hodge, Werner Fornos, Herman Daly, Stephen Schneider, and David Orr* (San Antonio, TX: Trinity University Press, 2005), Chapter 7: Living in a finite world: Herman Daly and economics, p. 132-163; Dietz, R. and O'Neill, D., *Enough is Enough: Building a Sustainable Economy in a World of Finite Resources* (San Francisco: Berrett-Koehler Publishers, 2013); Czech, B., *Supply Shock: Economic Growth at the Crossroads and the Steady State Solution* (Gabriola Island, BC: New Society Publishers, 2013).

Pg 122: Heilbroner quote ("[The necessity of economists] waited upon the ... best monetary advantage") from Heilbroner, R.L., *The Worldly Philosophers: The Lives, Times, and Ideas of the Great Economic Thinkers*, 7th edition (New York: Touchstone, 1999), p. 20.

Pg 123: Smith quote ("Every individual ... intends to promote it") from Smith, A., *The Wealth of Nations* (1776) and discussed at http://en. wikipedia.org/wiki/The_Wealth_of_Nations [accessed 16 October 2013].

The history of economic thought is found in Heilbroner, *The Worldly Philosophers*.

Neoclassical economics is discussed in Daly and Cobb, Jr., *For the Common Good*; Daly and Farley, *Ecological Economics*; Gowdy and O'Hara, *Economic Theory for Environmentalists*.

Pg 124: Discussions of the economy as the whole with the environment (natural world) merely supplying inputs and economics as a science can be found in McDaniel, *Wisdom for a Livable Planet*, p. 132-163.

Pg 125: 11.1, © Donald Watson illustration.

Pg 126: Gowdy and McDaniel quote ("The self-organizing principles ... human-created economic systems") from Gowdy, J.M. and McDaniel, C.N. "One world, one experiment: addressing the biodiversity-economics conflict," *Ecological Economics* 15 (1995), p. 181.

The story of Nauru is given in McDaniel and Gowdy, *Paradise for Sale*.

Pg 127: Assessing the carrying capacity of Earth is difficult at best; however, the fact that humans are affecting significantly geological cycles (e.g., carbon, nitrogen, water cycles), changing the climate, and causing impoverishment and loss of myriad ecosystems and species leaves little question that at 7 billion we have significantly overshot Earth's capacity to support human activities. This is affirmed by assessments of the human ecological footprint presented in Wackernagel, M. and Rees, W., *Our Ecological Footprint: Reducing Human Impact on the Earth* (Gabriola Island, BC: New Society Publishers, 1996) and at http://www.footprintnetwork. org/en/index.php/gfn/page/footprint_basics_overview/ [accessed 16 October 2013].

Pg 128:   The steady-state economy is discussed in Daly, H., *Beyond Growth: The Economics of Sustainable Development* (Boston: Beacon Press, 1996).

Daly quote (1. Exploit renewable resources … assimilated by ecosystems) from Daly, H., "Toward some operational principles of sustainable development," *Ecological Economics* 2 (1990), p. 1-6.

Detailed discussion of reasons for and the achieving of a steady-state economy is found in Dietz and O'Neill, *Enough is Enough*; Czech, *Supply Shock*.

Pg 129:   Annual United States and world meat consumption numbers from http://www.npr.org/blogs/thesalt/2012/06/27/155527365/visualizing-a-nation-of-meat-eaters [accessed 16 October 2013].

Annual United States sugar consumption numbers from http://www.nytimes.com/2012/10/27/business/us-cuts-estimate-of-sugar-intake-of-typical-american.html?pagewanted=all [accessed 16 October 2013].

Annual United States gasoline consumption numbers from http://www.eia.gov/tools/faqs/faq.cfm?id=23&t=10 [accessed 16 October 2013].

Annual United States BTU numbers from http://www.eia.gov/totalenergy/data/annual/pdf/sec1_3.pdf [accessed 16 October 2013].

Annual world BTU numbers from http://www.eia.gov/tools/faqs/faq.cfm?id=87&t=1 [accessed 16 October 2013].

Chapter 12: Leadership and Durable Societies

Shackleton's leadership genius was the subject of two books that I found useful in writing this chapter: Perkins, D.N.T., *Leading at the Edge: Leadership Lessons from the Extraordinary Saga of Shackleton's Antarctic Expedition* (New York: AMCOM, 2000); and Morrell, M. and Capparell, S., *Shackleton's Way: Leadership Lessons from the Great Antarctic Explorer* (New York: Viking, 2001).

Pg 132: Quote ("On one side … books on navigation) from Morrell and Capparell, *Shackleton's Way*, p. 26.

Shackleton quote ("So now we'll go home") from Perkins, *Leading at the Edge*, p. 16.

Shackleton quote ("A man must … goes to ground") from Shackleton, E., *South: The Last Antarctic Expedition of Shackleton and the* Endurance (New York: The Lyons Press, 1998), p. 77.

Pg 134: Quote ("the life and soul") from Morrell and Capparell, *Shackleton's Way*, p. 26.

Quote ("[Everything] is most carefully … the next man's helping") from Shackleton, *South*, p. 91.

Pg 135: Perkins quote ("In my search … leadership and teamwork") from Perkins, *Leading at the Edge*, p. xvii-xviii.

Pg 136: First summary of the genetic basis for human behavior from Wilson, E.O., *Sociobiology: The New Synthesis* (Cambridge, MA: Harvard University Press, 1975), Chapter 27: Man: from sociobiology to sociology, p. 547-575.

Quote ("Wilson you're all wet") from http://www.nytimes.com/books/98/12/06/specials/wilson-naturalist.html [accessed 16 October 2013].

An overview of human nature can be found in Wilson, E.O., *On Human Nature* (Cambridge, MA: Harvard University Press, 1978); Degler, C.N., *In Search of Human Nature: The Decline and Revival of Darwinism in American Social Thought* (New York: Oxford University Press, 1991); Wilson, E.O., *Consilience* (New York: Knopf, 1998); Morrison, R., *The Spirit in the Gene: Humanity's Proud Illusion and the Laws of Nature* (Ithaca, NY: Cornell University Press, 1999); Low, B.S., *Why Sex Matters: A Darwinian Look at Human Behavior* (Princeton, NJ: Princeton University Press, 2000); Ehrlich, P.R., *Human Natures: Genes, Cultures, and the Human Prospect* (Washington, DC: Island Press, 2000); Pinker, S., *The Blank Slate:The Modern Denial of Human Nature* (New York: Allen Lane, 2002); Wilson, E.O., *The Social Conquest of Earth* (New York: Liverright Publishing Company, 2012).

Pg 137: *Endurance* Party pay scale is from Lansing, A., Endurance*: Shackleton's Incredible Voyage* (New York: Caroll & Graf Publishers, 1959), p. 15-16.

The highest CEOs in the United States from http://www.forbes.com/lists/2012/12/ceo-compensation-12_rank.html [accessed 16 October 2013].

Pg 138: The most equitable societies deliver the highest quality of life is from Wilkinson, F.G. and Pickett, K., *The Spirit Level: Why More Equal Societies Almost Always Do Better* (New York: Allen Lane, 2009).

CEO and average worker pay ratios: 11/1 Japan, 475/1 US from http://creativeconflictwisdom.wordpress.com/2011/10/07/ration-of-ceo-pay-to-average-worker-by-country/ [accessed 16 October 2013].

Pg 139: Egalitarian behavior of hunter-gatherers from Gowdy, J. (Ed.), *Limited Wants, Unlimited Means: A Hunter-Gatherer Reader on Economics and the Environment* (Washington, DC: Island Press, 1998).

Coda

Pg 141: Carbon dioxide reaches atmospheric concentration of 400 ppm from http://blogs.scientificamerican.com/observations/2013/05/09/400-ppm-carbon-dioxide-in-the-atmosphere-reaches-prehistoric-levels/ [accessed 17 October 2013].

Pg 142: The majority of people in the world do not accept Darwinian evolution as the explanation by which humans came into existence from http://en.wikipedia.org/wiki/Level_of_support_for_evolution; http://www.huffingtonpost.com/2012/06/05/americans-believe-in-creationism_n_1571127.html; http://www.newyorker.com/online/ blogs/frontal-cortex/2012/06/brain-experiments-why-we-dont-believe-science.html [accessed 17 October 2013].

Information on the Standard Social Science Model can be found in http://www.themindevolution.com/2010/08/30/how-to-explain-human-nature-evolution-or-standard-social-science-model/ and http://en.wikipedia.org/wiki/Standard_social_science_model; http://www.goldmark.org/jeff/papers/ridley/html/node1.html [accessed 17 October 2013].

Pg 143: Pinker, S., *The Blank Slate: The Modern Denial of Human Nature* (New York: Allen Lane, 2002).

Information on Lysenko and pseudoscience in Soviet Union can be found in Soyfer, V.N., *Lysenko and the Tragedy of Soviet Science* (New Brunswick, NJ: Rutgers University Press, 1994), translated from Russian by Leo Gruliow and Rebecca Gruliow; McDaniel, C.N., "The human cost of ideology as science," *Conservation Biology* 18(4) (2004), p. 1-3.

Pg 144: Discussion of spirituality and religion as elements of human nature are found in Wilson, D.S., *Darwin's Cathedral: Evolution, Religion, and the Nature of Society* (Chicago: University of Chicago Press, 1992); Wilson, E.O., *Consilience* (New York: Knopf, 1998); Hamer, D., *The God Gene: How Faith Is Hardwired into Our Genes* (New York; Doubleday, 2004).Wade, N., *The Faith Instinct: How Religion Evoluted & Why It Persists* (New York: The Penguin Press, 2009).

Discussion of our ancestors is found in Sagan, C. and Druyan, A., *Shadows of Forgotten Ancestors: A Search for Who We Are* (New York: Random House, 1992).

Discussions on transcendental and empirical worldviews are given in Sagan, C., *The Demon-Haunted World: Science as a Candle in the Dark* (New York: Random House, 1995) and Wilson, E.O., *Consilience: The Unity of Knowledge* (New York: Knoph, 1998).

Darwin's most important books are in Wilson, E.O. (Ed.), *From So Simple a Beginning: The Four Great Books of Charles Darwin* (New York: Norton, 2004).

Pg 145: Wilson quote ("The great naturalist ... the laws of nature") from Wilson, *From So Simple a Beginning*, p. 1482-1483.

Discussion of religion and science are found in Sagan, C., *The Varieties of Scientific Experience: A Personal View of the Search for God* (New York: Penguin, 2006).

The preface to Dowd, M., *Thank God for Evolution: How the Marriage of Science and Religion Will Transform Your Life and Our World* (New York: Viking, 2010) is given at http://evolutionarytimes.org/?id= 286312 9613521652787 [accessed 16 October 2013].

Dowd quote ("Ecology is the new ... egregious of ways") from *Huffington Post*, 14 March 2013 (http://www.huffingtonpost.com/rev-michael-dowd/ [accessed 16 October 2013]).

Pg 146: Berry quote ("[T]he existing religious ... story of the universe") from Berry, T., *Dream of the Earth*, (San Francisco: Sierra Club Books, 1988), p. 87.

Berry quote ("The Great Work now ... functioning of the planet") from Berry, T., *The Great Work: Our Way into the Future* (New York: Bell Tower, 1999), p. 31.

Pg 147: Wade quote ("[A] typical tribal society ... killed on the spot") from Wade, *The Faith Instinct*, p. 49.

Discussion of the categorization of people can be found in Berreby, D., *Us & Them: The Science of Identity* (Chicago: Chicago University Press, 2005).

Discussion of the evolution of unselfish behavior can be found in Sober, E. and Wilson, D.S., *Unto Others: The Evolution and Psychology of Unselfish Behavior* (Cambridge, MA: Harvard University Press, 1999).

Pg 148: Shackleton quote ("the largest and ... crossing of the continent") from Lansing, A., Endurance: *Shackleton's Incredible Voyage* (New York: Caroll & Graf Publishers, 1959), p. 11.

Subject Index

175

Names Index

ABOUT THE AUTHOR

Carl N. McDaniel is Visiting Professor at Oberlin College in Oberlin, Ohio, and Professor Emeritus at Rensselaer Polytechnic Institute in Troy, New York. He was founding director of the undergraduate environmental science degree program at Rensselaer. For the first three decades of his academic career he researched insect and then plant development. His scholarly interests since have focused on the interface between biology and economics. He has written three books—*Paradise for Sale: A Parable of Nature* (2000, with economist John M. Gowdy), *Wisdom for a Livable Planet: The Visionary Work of Terri Swearingen, Dave Foreman, Wes Jackson, Helena Norberg-Hodge, Werner Fornos, Herman Daly, Stephen Schneider, and David Orr* (2005) and *Trail Magic: Creating a Positive Energy Home* (2012).